GOD TEMPERS THE WIND TO THE SHORN LAMB

About the **Translator**: **Marc Linder**, who taught on the social science faculty at Roskilde University in Denmark for three years, has translated two volumes of German fiction—Johannes Bobrowski, *I Taste Bitterness* (Seven Seas Publishers, 1970), and Fred Wander, *The Seventh Well* (Seven Seas Publishers, 1976)—and was certified as a simultaneous interpreter for Danish and German by the U.S. State Department. After graduate studies in Göttingen and Berlin and receiving a Ph.D. in political science at Princeton University, he worked at Hohenheim University in Germany and the National Autonomous University of Mexico. A graduate of Harvard Law School, he represented migrant farm workers in the Rio Grande Valley for seven years on behalf of Texas Rural Legal Aid before becoming a professor of labor law at the University of Iowa. Among his fifteen books are *"Moments Are the Elements of Profit": Overtime and the Deregulation of Working Hours under the Fair Labor Standards Act* (Fănpìhuà Press, 2000); *Wars of Attrition: Vietnam, the Business Roundtable, and the Decline of Construction Unions* (2d ed; Fănpìhuà Press, 2000 [1999]); *Of Cabbages and Kings County: Agriculture and the Formation of Modern Brooklyn* (University of Iowa Press, 1999), which received the Saloutos Prize for the best book in agricultural history; and *Void Where Prohibited: Rest Breaks and the Right to Urinate on Company Time* (Cornell University Press, 1998).

About the **Assistant: Gitte Gaarsvig Sørensen** works at a publishing house in the central Jutland town of Herning.

About the **Publisher**: **Fănpìhuà Press**, which accepts no revenue, publishes works that profit-driven university presses refuse to consider. Fănpìhuà Press also publishes Linder's translations of Hans Kirk's *The Fishermen* (ISBN 0-9673899-2-5), *The Slave* (ISBN 0-9673899-4-1), and *The Day Laborers* and *The New Times* (ISBN 0-9673899-6-8), and Klitgaard's *There's a Man Sitting on a Trolley* (ISBN 0-9673899-7-6). Its books are distributed by Iowa Book & Supply at (319) 337-4188 or iowabook@iowabook.com and Prairie Lights Books at (800) 295-BOOK or info@prairielights.com

Mogens Klitgaard

God Tempers the Wind to the Shorn Lamb

Translated and
with an Introduction and Notes
by Marc Linder

With the Assistance of
Gitte Gaarsvig Sørensen

Fănpìhuà Press
Iowa City
2002

Printed in the United States of America

Translated from the first edition of Mogens Klitgaard, *Gud mildner luften for de klippede faar* (Copenhagen: Povl Branner, 1938).

The cover image is one of the friezes adorning the lobby of the Danish Parliament, which were painted by Rasmus Larsen between 1918 and 1921. Courtesy of Folketinget.

Suggested Library of Congress Cataloging
Klitgaard, Mogens, 1906-1945
God tempers the wind to the shorn lamb/by Mogens Klitgaard. Translated and with an Introduction and Notes by Marc Linder
xxv, 148 p.; 21 cm.
Includes bibliographical references
ISBN 0-9673899-8-4
PT8175.K56 G813 2002
Library of Congress Preassigned Control Number: 2002090817

Contents

Introduction[1]

A . . . sturdy vagabond . . . shall at the first time be whipped, and sent to the place where he was born or last dwelled . . ., there to get his living; and if he continue his roguish life, he shall have the upper part of the gristle of his right ear cut off; and if after that he be taken wandering in idleness, or doth not apply to his labour, or is not in service with any master, he shall be adjudged and executed as a felon.[2]

This tale of a young Dane's life as a vagabond in post-World War I Europe is, more or less, the true story of Mogens Klitgaard from the age of sixteen to his mid-twenties. Ironically, the laudatory review of the Danish original in the *Times Literary Supplement* failed to understand its autobiographical character; instead, the anonymous reviewer mistakenly believed that the book focused on a "tramp, whom the author meets . . . and whose confidence he wins by standing him a meal."[3] In fact, the author is the tramp and the man who buys him coffee merely a stage prop.

The prehistory of Klitgaard's vagabondage during the 1920s is an interesting story in its own right. Perhaps the most signifi-

---

[1]In addition to new material, this Introduction includes an abbreviated and revised version of Marc Linder, "Introduction," in Mogens Klitgaard, *There's a Man Sitting on a Trolley* vii-xxxviii (Marc Linder tr.; Iowa City: Fănpìhuà, 2001).

[2]28 Henry VIII ch. 25 § 3 (1535), in *The Statutes at Large from the First Year of King Richard III. to the Thirty-First Year of King Henry VIII. inclusive*, vol. V:387, 388 (Danby Pickering ed.; Cambridge: Bentham, 1763).

[3]"The Problem Child: A New Novelist from the Faroes," *Times Literary Supplement*, Foreign Books Section, Quarterly Survey, No. 3, Mar. 1939, at v. Though brief, the review praised Klitgaard for telling a "good, convincing story in an excellent style . . . ."

cant departure from autobiographical reality was that Klitgaard's real father was not a parish deacon. Klitgaard was born into a middle-class family in Valby, an industrializing village that had been incorporated into Copenhagen five years before his birth in 1906. His father, Emanuel Klitgaard, was a department head of the umbrella organization of the Danish consumer co-operative stores and conductor of its amateur orchestra. Emanuel Klitgaard appears to have been a good burgher and religiously oriented, but whether he had institutionalized church connections is, given the dearth of source materials, unknown. Mogens Klitgaard's secure childhood began to crumble in 1913 at the age of six when his mother died of cancer; three years later he had become an orphan when his father also died of cancer. After briefly living with his stepmother—his father had married the family's maid the year after his wife's death—who had never shown any interest in him or his older sister, he moved in with his aunt and uncle. Though fond of him, the childless couple did not feel equal to the task of being parents and in 1917 they placed him in the Royal Orphanage in Copenhagen.[4]

This harsh and highly structured total institution, which enforced obedience, punctuality, and order by corporal punishment and detention, thus preventing Klitgaard from spending weekends with his aunt and uncle and brother and sister, imbued this wilful child, known as an "escape artist" since the age of four,

---

[4]B[ertel Bing], "Ligefremt Interview: Virkelig Romantik i Hverdagslivet," *Nationaltidende*, June 10, 1937; *Dansk biografisk leksikon* 8:41 (Copenhagen: Gyldendal, 1981); Leon Jaurnow, "Drømmen om noget andet—portræt af Mogens Klitgaard i anledning af 50-året for hans død," in *Magasin fra Det kongelige bibliotek* 10:3-14 at 4 (1995); Leon Jaurnow, "Efterskrift," in Mogens Klitgaard, *Der sidder en mand i en sporvogn* 193-209 at 202 (N.p.: Dansk Lærerforeningen, 1997); Leon Jaurnow, *Den lyse vagabond: Mogens Klitgaards liv og forfatterskab* 8-11 (Copenhagen: Reitzel, 2002 [forthcoming]); telephone interview with Inga Klitgaard (May 25, 2001).

with an exceedingly intense desire for freedom.[5]

At the end of the summer of 1921, at the age of fourteen, he was placed out as a market-gardener's apprentice in Rødvig, a town about 40 miles south of Copenhagen, where he was supposed to work for five years. The choice had not been his: the orphanage and his brother Svend, who was ten years older and acted as a kind of guardian, had chosen the apprenticeship for him. He had never wished to become a gardener and never cared a bit for the "hard toil of an unskilled laborer from morning till evening"; but being an orphan, he had to go someplace where he would not be a burden to anyone. For his 12-hour workday the young Klitgaard received room and board and 10 crowns per month.[6]

In the spring of 1922 he engaged in his first act of "rebellion"—flight. One day he got into a dispute with the market-gardener, hopped on to a bicycle, and headed to Elsinore about 70 miles away; after stopping in Copenhagen to telephone his family to inform them of his decision, he bicycled up the Zealand coast and crossed over to Sweden, making his way north. Initially he made a living dealing in notions and working for a farmer.[7] At the age of fifteen he had thus embarked on a vaga-

---

[5]Jaurnow, *Den lyse vagabond* at 12-17.

[6]Mow., "Min Bog var for mig Knald eller Fald—siger Mogens Klitgaard," *Berlingske Aftenavis*, June 9, 1937; Christian Houmark, "Daarligt egnet til at møde Livet," *B.T.*, June 10, 1937; Mogens Klitgaard, "En Søndag for to Aar siden," *Berlingske Aftenavis*, Dec. 8, 1938 (quote); Jaurnow, "Drømmen om noget andet" at 4, 6; Jaurnow, *Den lyse vagabond* at 18-19, 27.

[7]Mow., "Min Bog var for mig Knald eller Fald—siger Mogens Klitgaard"; Houmark, "Daarligt egnet til at møde Livet"; Klitgaard, "En Søndag for to Aar siden"; Jaurnow, "Drømmen om noget andet" at 4, 6; Jaurnow, *Den lyse vagabond* at 22-23. According to Jaurnow, "Efterskrift" at 204, Klitgaard stopped a few miles south of Elsinore at Humlebæk, sneaked on to a stolen boat and sailed to Sweden. Klitgaard

bondage that would last a decade.

His "rebellion," as Klitgaard explained to an interviewer after the appearance of his first novel, was against "the whole thing," though not actually against "society." On the one hand he was driven by a "longing to go abroad" to see and experience; on the other hand, his life was "extremely depressing" because he simply lacked the money to buy himself "anything new" and get out and about like the other young people.[8]

The opening line of *God Tempers the Wind to the Shorn Lamb* (p. 3) may have declared that he sometimes believed that chance occurrences do not determine our lives, but his own life would probably have followed a radically different course had his brother Svend, instead of giving him a one-way train ticket to Rødvig, helped him realize his wish of becoming a clerical trainee at the Copenhagen office of the East Asiatic Company (Denmark's premier agent of colonial exploitation) with prospects of being stationed under the Orient's green palms and baking sun.[9]

About Klitgaard's decade-long vagabondage, which began in 1922, something is known from the entries in his diary, which dates from 1926 and is archived at the Royal Library in Copenhagen. Between 1922 and 1932 Klitgaard lived in Sweden, Norway, Germany, France, and England, working as a seaman, smuggler, counterman, waiter, dishwasher, office worker, farm worker, and "agitation leader in a revolutionary organization," though he never held a permanent job and worked from one day to the next. In between he also returned for various periods of time to Copenhagen, where, for example, in 1923 he worked at

---

did not mention this boat theft in the aforementioned autobiographical accounts, but the narrator recounts the incident in *God Tempers the Wind to the Shorn Lamb*, p. 5.

[8]Houmark, "Daarligt egnet til at møde Livet."

[9]Jaurnow, *Den lyse vagabond* at 27.

a dairy, and sometimes lived on public assistance and ate at the people's kitchen, where his alter ego tells his tale to a stranger in the novel.[10] At the end of 1923 he travelled to Sweden again, but returned to Copenhagen in the following years, where he worked as a delivery boy and also lived on public assistance again. In 1927-28 he was in Marseille, Nice, and Paris, washing dishes and pretending to be a globetrotter. By 1929 he was back in Copenhagen working at a billiard parlor and suffering from tuberculosis.[11]

His "greatest experience" as a vagabond was to lie on his back by the roadside, "just staring up into the air, being completely free and independent, completely without responsibility, without obligations. Freer than the birds, which have a nest and mate and chicks and all that stuff" (p. 36). It was an attitude that reappeared in other novels too. Even in his posthumously published science-fiction novel written in 1932-33, Klitgaard called "lying by the roadside staring up at the blue sky with the drifting clouds . . . paradise on earth."[12]

The problem, however, was that Klitgaard soon discovered that gazing at the sky from a horizontal position was not possible that often—even for a vagabond. Not only did the danger of getting work lurk everywhere, but life as a vagabond became just as monotonous as work in a factory or office. That routine reached its absurdist high point when Klitgaard wound up running a bureaucratically organized cigarette smuggling business on the northern Norwegian-Swedish border—an activity that came to an end in November 1924 when the Swedish police arrested and

---

[10]Mow., "Min Bog var for mig Knald eller Fald—siger Mogens Klitgaard"; Klitgaard, "En Søndag for to Aar siden"; Ebbe Neergaard, *Mogens Klitgaard* 5 (Copenhagen: Carit Andersen, 1941); Jaurnow, *Den lyse vagabond* at 23.

[11]Jaurnow, *Den lyse vagabond* at 22-40.

[12]Mogens Klitgaard, *de sindssyges klode* 68 (Copenhagen: Carit Andersen, 1968).

deported him to Copenhagen for being unable to support himself. He was just as unable to support himself in Denmark delivering groceries, but at least he was not subject to deportation and could obtain public assistance.[13]

Klitgaard's involuntary relapses into work—which the vagabond in *God Tempers the Wind to the Shorn Lamb* attributes to the lingering influence of his petty-bourgeois upbringing—points up how Klitgaard straddled the borders marking off vagabonds, hobos, and tramps. Because the term "vagabond," as the standard U.S. legal dictionary observes, "became archaic" during the course of the twentieth century—"as vagrants won the right not to be forcibly removed from cities," vagabonds in the 1980s and 1990s "came to be known as street people and homeless people, or the homeless"[14]—vagabondage must be seen in its historical context.

True to its roots in the Latin verb "to wander," the word "vagabond" has come to mean one with a "carefree fondness for a roaming life." In contrast, the late-nineteenth-century western American word "hobo" "sometimes implies a willingness to work, sometimes suggests travel by freight trains, and is often applied to a migratory worker who follows seasonal occupations." Finally, a "tramp" "lives by wandering whether in search of transient work or engaged in begging or petty thievery."[15] Like the vagabondizing Klitgaard himself, the word "vagabond" in the *Oxford English Dictionary* partakes of all these dimen-

---

[13]Mogens Klitgaard, "Teddy-Smugleren," in Mogens Klitgaard, *Hverdagens musik: Udvalgte noveller og skitser* at 27-34 (Sven Møller Kristensen ed.; n.p. [Copenhagen]: Fremad, 1989); Jaurnow, *Den lyse vagabond* at 30.

[14]*Black's Law Dictionary* 1547 (Bryan Garner ed.; St. Paul: West, 1999).

[15]*Webster's Third New International Dictionary of the English Language Unabridged* 2528, col. 1 (Springfield, Mass.: Merriam-Webster, 1993) (s.v. "vagabond").

sions too: "itinerant beggar, idle loafer, or tramp; vagrant."[16]

These definitions, subtle as they may be, neglect the socio-historical background and brutal suppression of vagabondage over the course of centuries. In Karl Marx's searing indictment, the dissolution of feudal retainers and the violent expulsion from the land by expropriation turned the expellees whom the rising manufactures could not absorb into a proletariat. Those who were unable to accommodate the discipline required by the new conditions were massively transformed into "beggars, robbers, vagabonds, in part from inclination, in most cases by the force of circumstances. Hence at the end of the 15th and during the whole of the 16th century in all of Western Europe a bloody legislation against vagabondage." These laws treated them as "'voluntary' criminals" and assumed that whether they kept on "working under the old conditions that no longer existed" depended on "their good will."[17]

The barbarity of the English legislation is exemplified with all imaginable clarity in "An act for the punishing of vagabonds" from 1547, which declared that "idleness and vagabondry is the mother and root of all thefts, robberies, and all evil acts . . . and the multitude of people given thereto hath always, been here within this realm very great, and more in number . . . than in other regions, to the great impoverishment of the realm and danger of the King's highness subjects . . . ." Because previous legislation had failed to repress them, "idle and vagabond persons being unprofitable members, or rather enemies of the common wealth, have been suffered to remain and increase, and yet so do, whom if they should be punished by death, whipping, imprison-

---

[16]*Oxford English Dictionary* 19:393, col. 1 (2d ed.; Oxford: Clarendon Press, 1989).

[17]Karl Marx, *Das Kapital: Kritik der politischen Oekonomie*. Erster Band: Buch I: *Der Produktionsprocess des Kapitals* 719 (Hamburg: Meissner, 1867).

ment, and with other corporal pain, it were not without their deserts, for the example of others . . . , yet if they could be brought to be made profitable, and do service, it were much to be wished and desired." To this beneficial end the act then provided:

If any person shall bring to two justices of peace, any runagate servant, or any other which liveth idly and loiteringly . . . the said justices shall cause the said . . . vagabond, to be marked with an hot iron on the breast, with the mark of *V* . . . and adjudge him to be slave to the same person . . . to have to him . . . for two years after, who shall take the said slave, and give him bread, water, or small drink, and refuse meat, and cause him to work, by beating, chaining or otherwise . . .: and if such slave absent himself from his said master . . . by the space of fourteen days, then he shall be adjudged by two justices of peace to be marked on the forehead, or the ball of the cheek, with an hot iron, with the sign of an *S* and further shall be adjudged to be slave to his said master for ever: . . . and if the said slave shall run away the second time, he shall be adjudged a felon.[18]

Into the early nineteenth century the British Parliament insisted on the deterrent value of publicly whipping vagrants until their backs were bloody, although some justices of the peace had refused to carry out this "intolerable barbarity."[19] Klitgaard's alter ego was imprisoned in England in the 1920s under the Vagrancy Act of 1824, which was still in effect,[20] and late into the twentieth century state penal codes in the United States contin-

---

[18]An act for the punishing of vagabonds, and for the relief of the poor and impotent persons, 1 Edward VI, ch. 3 (1547), in *The Statutes at Large, From the Thirty-Second Year of King Henry VIII. to the Seventh Year of King Edward VI. inclusive*, vol. V:246 (Danby Pickering ed.; Cambridge: Bentham, 1763).

[19]Sidney Webb and Beatrice Webb, *English Local Government: English Poor Law History*, Part I: *The Old Poor Law* 373-83 (quote at 375) (London: Longmans, Green, 1927).

[20]See below p. 141 (note to p. 84).

ued to impose up to six months of hard labor on those doing precisely what Klitgaard had been doing in the 1920s—"wandering about and lodging in barns . . . and having no visible calling or business to maintain themselves" or "begging in public places or from house to house."[21] And even in Klitgaard's Danish welfare state, hundreds of work-shy inmates were incarcerated in the 1920s and 1930s at Sundholm, Copenhagen's workhouse (*Arbejdsanstalt*) for younger able-bodied persons with a tendency to vagabondage and alcohol abuse.[22]

If Klitgaard's vagabondage, which resulted as much from inclination as rebellion, was, from a socio-economic perspective, "voluntary," his decision to leave the lumpenproletariat—which Marx defined as composed of vagabonds, criminals, and prostitutes[23]—was forced on him by his poor health. A turning point in his life took place in 1929, when he got a job as a scorekeeper-pinsetter at a billiard parlor in Copenhagen, his 70- to 84-hour workweek being compensated at a mere 30 crowns. That same year his failing health led to his rejection as a soldier, and after having lived outdoors for a decade, he was even more vulnerable to the smoky indoor air. On New Year's Eve 1932 he was admitted on an emergency basis to the tuberculosis ward of a Copenhagen municipal hospital; in March he was transferred to the tuberculosis sanatorium at Boserup near Roskilde, where he remained a patient for five months.[24]

---

[21]Iowa Code, §§ 746.1.3-.4. and 746.15 (1975). The legislature repealed this provision in 1976.

[22]For data and sources, see the annotation in Klitgaard, *There's a Man Sitting on a Trolley* at 180-81.

[23]Marx, *Das Kapital* at 630.

[24]Mow., "Min Bog var for mig Knald eller Fald—siger Mogens Klitgaard" (70 hours); Klitgaard, "En Søndag for to Aar siden" (84 hours); Jaurnow, *Den lyse vagabond* at 40, 44, 57. According to Klitgaard's own account, he began working as a scorekeeper in 1932, but his biographer insists that Klitgaard's own diary notes show that his

While there he became an avid and voracious reader, especially fascinated by the American novelists Dos Passos, Hemingway, and F. Scott Fitzgerald, in addition to Ilya Ehrenburg, Erich Kästner, B. Traven, Hans Kirk, and Martin Andersen Nexø.[25] During his stay at the sanatorium he also wrote his first book, the aforementioned socialist science-fiction novel (*The Globe of the Insane*) about a scientific expedition to another planet. Through a common friend in left-wing cultural circles, Klitgaard sent the manuscript to Hans Kirk, who in 1928 had published his first novel, *The Fishermen*, to critical acclaim, and was already a critic of note. On July 2, 1934, Kirk replied to the friend: "There's no doubt that he has talent." Although the book was "handsomely and sensibly" constructed, Kirk had two crucial objections: Klitgaard's language was academically dry and stiff and his dialogs old-fashionedly bookish, and the psychological conflict too slight and uninteresting. The decisive point for Kirk was whether Klitgaard could train his psychological sense. In addition to vigilantly observing himself and others, he advised Klitgaard to "study modern psychology—Freud."[26]

Klitgaard respected Kirk's opinion so highly that he put the manuscript away, never showed it to anyone, and never published it.[27] As its posthumous publication in 1968 revealed, Kirk and Klitgaard were right: though the novel was not uninteresting, its scarcely veiled indirect critique of conditions on Earth was

---

memory later failed him. Email from Leon Jaurnow (June 1, 2001).

[25]Poul Carit Andersen, "Mogens Klitgaard," in Klitgaard, *de sindssyges klode* 5-28 at 13; Jaurnow, "Drømmen om noget andet" at 8, 10.

[26]Letter from Hans Kirk to Helge Andersen (July 2, 1934), in Mogens Klitgaard's papers, Det kongelige Bibliotek (Copenhagen), NKS 2839, 2 (copy furnished by Leon Jaurnow).

[27]This account is based on the forthcoming biography of Klitgaard by Leon Jaurnow, who has studied Klitgaard's papers at the Royal Library in Copenhagen.

tediously heavy-handed.[28] None of Klitgaard's published novels ever displayed such flaws.

After he was discharged from the sanatorium in 1933, Klitgaard's health was no longer robust enough to permit him to resume his vagabondage. But he returned to his old job as billiard scorekeeper,[29] where he met an interesting cross-section of the Copenhagen populace, who provided him with rich material for his first published novel. He also became involved in left-wing political organizations and the Danish Communist Party's Red Aid (which assisted communist refugees), of which he became secretary. Klitgaard, however, never joined the party itself because he wished to retain his independence.[30]

How Klitgaard became a novelist is bound up with his vagabondage. According to accounts he gave in 1937 and 1938, on turning 30 in 1936 he "felt a beginning self-contempt"[31] in taking a quick survey of the insignificant way his life had passed until then: "the course of events painted a picture of a weak person, a person who was seeking freedom, but who'd never been so far removed from freedom as now." But he "actually couldn't see where the mistake lay, on which occasion or occasions he should have behaved differently." Though people do do things which in their consequences turn out to have been wrong, "taking into account the situation, taking into account my nature, my upbringing, and my morality, I couldn't perceive the great, decisive mistake I must have committed." The fear and agitation un-

---

[28]Klitgaard, *de sindssyges klode*. For a different view, see *Dansk litteraturhistorie*, vol. 7: *Demokrati og kulturkamp 1901-45*, at 436 (Copenhagen: Gyldendal, 1984) (chapter written by Ib Bondebjerg).

[29]Mow., "Min Bog var for mig Knald eller Fald—siger Mogens Klitgaard"; Jaurnow, "Efterskrift" at 206.

[30]Carit Andersen, "Mogens Klitgaard" at 14; Jaurnow, *Den lyse vagabond* at 59-63; telephone interviews with Inga Klitgaard and Leon Jaurnow (May 25, 2001).

[31]Houmark, "Daarligt egnet til at møde Livet."

leashed by his thirtieth birthday suddenly came over him as he was sitting in Kongens Nytorv—one of Copenhagen's most popular squares—one Sunday afternoon in the late summer of 1936. Klitgaard imagined that in "semi-elegant and awfully boring" Kongens Nytorv the frayed edges on his pants were the most conspicuous ones there to the "boring middle-class people whose sole ambition was to rise to a higher social level." It was not the frayed edges per se he cared about, but only as an expression of the unfreedom in which he found himself at a time when he still suffered from the illusion that people who wandered the roads were free, although in fact no one was more dependent on his surroundings than a beggar. Sitting there, he recalled one morning in the 1920s when, penniless in Paris, he had been on the way to sign up for the Foreign Legion; by sheer coincidence he ran into a Dane who lent him 100 francs and persuaded him not to join. Realizing that his whole life had consisted of lucky and unlucky coincidences, he left Kongens Nytorv, went home, and began writing *There's a Man Sitting on a Trolley*[32]—a satirical yet sympathetic account of the pathetically absurd efforts of a bankrupt Copenhagen dry-goods storekeeper to maintain his middle-class aspirations by working as a door-to-door bill collector during the Great Depression.

He began work on the novel in November 1936 and, despite the time-consuming demands of his job and having only enough money to buy 25 sheets of paper at a time, he was able to complete it by January 1937. After hand-delivering it to a publishing house, he went home, and impatiently waited for a response, especially since a turn for the worse in his health had forced him to work half-time at a wage that failed to cover even his modest needs. The manuscript was accepted and the book appeared in June 1937.[33]

---

[32]Klitgaard, "En Søndag for to Aar siden."

[33]Mow., "Min Bog var for mig Knald eller Fald—siger Mogens

Publication of the book, Klitgaard told an interviewer, meant more to him than anyone imagined. Writing it had not been driven by "literary ambition"; rather it was "make or break" for his life.[34] Critics "unanimously praised"[35] the novel as a "brilliant debut." It became "the book of the year," receiving "the most laudatory reviews" of any debut novel in "many years" and going through four printings in three or four months.[36] Klitgaard was able to give notice at the billiard parlor. Soon he was asked to give readings and excerpts from the novel were read on Danish state radio.[37]

The following year Klitgaard published *God Tempers the Wind to the Shorn Lamb,* which Hans Kirk's review in the communist paper *Arbejderbladet* praised as an "artistic triumph." Here Kirk drew out the dichotomous political consequences of the petty-bourgeois upbringing that forms the novel's centerpiece: "Bourgeoisness or anarchism. Parish deacon or vagabond." Kirk ultimately agreed with Klitgaard, whom he called "talented, funny and full of feeling, smart and controlled," that, when petty-bourgeois morality bursts, people who, like the vagabond, had been trapped in it without developing a broader view of society, run the risk of ending up in emotional anarchy.[38]

In a second review of *God Tempers the Wind to the Shorn*

Klitgaard"; Klitgaard, "En Søndag for to Aar siden"; Carit Andersen, "Mogens Klitgaard" at 17; Neergaard, *Mogens Klitgaard* at 8.

[34]Mow., "Min Bog var for mig Knald eller Fald—siger Mogens Klitgaard."

[35]Mow., "Min Bog var for mig Knald eller Fald—siger Mogens Klitgaard."

[36]Carit Andersen, "Mogens Klitgaard" at 18, 5; Jaurnow, *Den lyse vagabond* at 77.

[37]Jaurnow, *Den lyse vagabond* at 78-79, 83.

[38]Hans Kirk, "Opgør med Borgerligheden," in Hans Kirk, *Litteratur og tendens: Essays og artikler* 107-11 at 107, 109 (Børge Houmann ed.; Copenhagen: Gyldendal, 1974 [Oct. 30, 1938]).

Lamb, which he praised for being "witty, elegant, and charming" and a "humoristic elegiac" treatment of the lifelong consequences of petty-bourgeois upbringing, Kirk went so far as to speculate that "if Klitgaard had seized the opportunity, he would have become the favorite of reactionary criticism."[39] As a later literary historian formulated it: "If conservative, social-democratic, and communist critics of the '30s could not agree on anything else, in any case they could all see that Mogens Klitgaard was an unusual author, who deserved much praise."[40]

In quick succession, Klitgaard in 1940 went on to publish two anti-heroic, social-historical novels focusing on the lives of ordinary everyday people. *Ballade paa Nytorv* (*Hullabaloo in Nytorv*), takes place in Copenhagen about the time of Frederik V's death in 1766, while *De røde Fjer* (*The Red Feathers*), is set in 1807, at the time of the British bombardment of Copenhagen during the Napoleonic wars. Both novels required significant original research and were designed to shed light on contemporary Danish life.[41] In 1941 he published *Elly Petersen,* the first novel ever commissioned to be read on Danish state radio (and which was made into a film in 1944), a story, inspired by his wife's own life, about a young woman's move from the provinces to Copenhagen to seek her luck.[42] Klitgaard published his last novel in 1942, *Den guddommelige Hverdag* (*The Divine Weekday*), a kaleidoscopic, experimental novel with documentary montages of actual newspaper articles and advertisements

---

[39]Hans Kirk, "Af Efteraarets Literatur," *Kulturkampen* 5(1):14-15 at 15 (1939).

[40]Hans Rømeling, *"Den lille mand" i 30'ernes litteratur belyst gennem udvalgte værker* 100 (Copenhagen: Studenterrådet, 1974).

[41]Mogens Klitgaard, *De røde Fjer* (Copenhagen: Povl Branner, 1940); Mogens Klitgaard, *Ballade paa Nytorv* (Copenhagen: Povl Branner, 1940); Jaurnow, *Den lyse vagabond* at 100.

[42]Mogens Klitgaard, *Elly Petersen* (Copenhagen: Carit Andersen, n.d. [1967?] [1941]); Jaurnow, *Den lyse vagabond* at 119-20, 124.

about Copenhagen during the German occupation.[43]

On August 29, 1943, the day on which Nazi Germany, which had occupied Denmark on April 9, 1940, dissolved the Danish government, Klitgaard, who had been in the limelight as former secretary of *Røde Hjælp* and a member of the board of directors of the newly formed authors organization *Forfatterforbundet*, was in North Zealand; instead of returning to Copenhagen, he fled to Sweden, thus avoiding the fate of other board members who were interned by the Gestapo. He lived there, joined half a year later by his wife and young son, until the liberation of Denmark in May 1945. His decade of vagabondage, however, had taken its toll: after a year's illness in Sweden, the recurrence of tuberculosis led to the removal of one of his kidneys; he died of tuberculosis of the heart on December 23, 1945, at the age of thirty-nine.[44]

The death of such an energetic young author might prompt regret for all the novels that were lost to the world. But Klitgaard might never have written any more books anyway: on his return to Denmark he concluded that there were more important things to do than write or even read novels about a world that had been totally turned upside down and had silenced him. He imagined becoming a journalist travelling around Europe, meeting people, understanding their problems, and contributing to the discussion about reconstruction.[45]

To be sure, in his obituary Hans Kirk expressed the belief that it was just as certain that Klitgaard would have returned to literature, "where he belonged. It was the vagabond in him that

---

[43]Mogens Klitgaard, *Den guddommelige hverdag* (Copenhagen: Carit Andersen, 1975 [1942]).

[44]"Noter," *Politiken*, Dec. 24, 1945 (attached to the obituary by Tom Kristensen, "Den lyse Vagabond, Mogens Klitgaard død"); Jaurnow, *Den lyse vagabond* at 154-55.

[45]Neergaard, "Mogens Klitgaards Død"; Carit Andersen, "Mogens Klitgaard" at 26-27; Jaurnow, *Den lyse vagabond* at 152-54.

longed for freedom after the war's long confinement." Kirk also suggested that Klitgaard, who "had never let go of his revolutionary Marxist convictions," had the talent, linguistic artistry, and breadth of social view to have written "a novel of European stature."[46]

In his six years as a novelist during a very brief life, Mogens Klitgaard had in fact succeeded in writing six books that made him one of Denmark's most interesting social-critical realist and historical novelists of the interwar period. He has rightfully been called "[t]he central representative of the period's ironic-elegant everyday realism"[47] and "one of Danish realism's classics."[48]

---

[46]Kirk, "Mogens Klitgaard."

[47]*Dansk litteraturhistorie*, vol. 7: *Demokrati og kulturkamp 1901-45*, at 434.

[48]Sven Møller Kristensen, "Indledning," in Klitgaard, *Hverdagens musik: Udvalgte noveller og skitser* 7-11 at 7.

A Note on the Text

The translation follows the text of the first edition: Mogens Klitgaard, *Gud mildner Luften for de klippede Faar* (Copenhagen: Povl Branner, 1938). The novel was also reissued in 1956 and 1969 by Fremad and Carit Andersen, respectively.[1]

Although several of Klitgaard's novels have been translated into German, French, Swedish, and Dutch,[2] *There's a Man Sitting on a Trolley* was the first to appear in English. The only other translation of *God Tempers the Wind to the Shorn Lamb* was published in German in 1950.[3]

Because non-Danish readers will not be familiar with many of the novel's cultural, geographic, historical, and institutional references, annotations are provided at the back of the book. An asterisk after the name, word, or phrase indicates that it is annotated.

---

[1]The latter, paperback edition contains many typographical errors. Mogens Klitgaard, *Gud mildner luften for de klippede får* (Copenhagen: Carit Andersen, n.d. [1969]).

[2]*Dansk skønlitterært forfatterleksikon*, vol. II: *1900-1950*, at 125 (Svend Dahl ed.; Copenhagen: Pedersen, 1960).

[3]Mogens Klitgaard, *Gott mildert die Luft für die geschorenen Schafe* (tr. Emil Charlet; [East] Berlin: Lied der Zeit, 1950). This translation is marred by numerous absurd mistakes and omissions of whole sentences.

A Note on the Cover

The cover image, which includes the Danish title of the book, is one of the ornamental friezes that the painter Rasmus Larsen (1867-1950) painted in the lobby of the Danish parliament between 1918 and 1921. The public in Denmark viewed Larsen as wishing to console the taxpayers.[1] The frieze is especially relevant because, according to Inga Klitgaard, the author's widow, it was from the parliament building that he was acquainted with the saying.[2]

Bente Pedersen of the Library, Archives, and Information Department of the Danish Parliament provided a copy of the cover image, which is in the public domain.

---

[1]T. Vogel-Jørgensen *Bevingede ord* 342 (5th ed.; Copenhagen: Gad, 1975).

[2]Telephone interview with Inga Klitgaard (September 12, 2001).

Acknowledgments

Gitte Gaarsvig Sørensen's insistence on intensively involving herself in every phase of the translation more than justifies the appearance of her name on the title page—despite the absence of any solid evidence of her non-cyberspatial existence. Her unfailingly prompt and unstintingly attentive responses to hundreds of queries remain a monument to an unwonted kind of solidarity, the survival of which would surely please Mogens Klitgaard.

Inga Klitgaard provided information about the text. **Leon Jaurnow** made available his forthcoming biography of Klitgaard and his extensive knowledge of the text of the novel and its background. **Morten Thing** (Roskilde University) and **Prof. Hans Hertel** (Institute for Nordic Philology at Copenhagen University) answered questions about obscure Danish terms and institutions. **Jacob Wraae Nielsen** furnished a copy of his thesis on Klitgaard. **Eva Nancke** (Arbejderbevægelsens Bibliotek og Arkiv) sent hard-to-find materials about Danish history. **Mary Rumsey** (University of Minnesota Law Library) provided copies of Swedish and Danish statutes. **Ulla Sweedler** explained several Swedish terms. **Bob Ramsey** (University of Iowa) scanned in the cover illustration.

At the last minute, **Marjorie Rahe** mercilessly expunged uncolloquialisms. **Kristin Solli** (University of Iowa) explained some Norwegian customs, but, more importantly, also generously checked the entire translation against the Danish original, while poet **Jan Weissmiller** expeditiously edited the manuscript.

The publication of this annotated translation of an important interwar social novel coincides with and is part of the celebration of the ninetieth birthday of **Elias Bredsdorff**, the patron saint of English-language Danish-literature studies.

God Tempers the Wind to the Shorn Lamb

But one day the vineyard's laborers began to talk about toiling and drudging for a wretched wage, while the vineyard's owner lived in splendor and delight and amassed riches.

And they went to him and said: Behold, master, we tend to your vineyard so that it yields a rich harvest, yet we have not enough that we can satisfy our own hunger, while you live in luxury and amass riches.

And the vineyard's owner replied to them that happiness is not goods or gold and told them the story of the wise man who set out to find the world's happiest person. The wise man searched in palaces and castles, but did not find the one he was seeking. But behold, in a vineyard he found a poor laborer, the poorest of all—he owned not even a coat. And this one was the happiest.

And the lord of the vineyard scolded the discontented laborers and admonished them to bring up their children to live in humility and not to covet what God has given their neighbor.

And he admonished them to observe the law's and God's commandments and reminded them of the creator's forbearance and gentleness.

*And that they might remember his admonitions, he wrote above the gate to the vineyard: God tempers the wind to the shorn lamb.**

First Chapter

1

Sometimes I think about the fact that it's not the chance occurrences that determine our lives, but the way we react to the chance occurrences. No doubt many a time life's offered me a chance—I just wasn't capable of taking it. Conversely, many a time life's given me an opportunity to do something wrong and I've never neglected to avail myself of it. When I was a boy, I stole from my mother's household money when her purse was inadvertently left lying on the plate rack, and I used every opportunity to tell a lie and spin stories that were pure fabrication.

My father was a parish deacon* and my whole family consisted of nice people who never did anything wrong; every Sunday morning I went with my sister to Sunday school. I usually sat between my sister and a little girl named Lise, and she used to — —.

But why, by the way, should I be sitting and telling all this. Of what interest can it be to other people to hear about how it happened that a person of my age is sitting here in this place. In a moment the manager's going to come and say that I have to go, and that I can't sit here for hours on end without buying anything. Sit and take space away from other people. He's already been keeping an eye on me, and next time a patron comes balancing his cup of coffee without being able to find a seat, he'll come waddling in his white smock and prick my shoulder with his fat, red index finger. I'm accustomed to being able to sit for a couple of hours over a cup of coffee; if you haven't emptied your cup, of course they can't chase you out that easily, but this evening I needed the hot coffee so much that I drank the whole thing, and besides, there are so many people here because the weather's bad.

2

For two weeks I lived in a rusted-out crate of an automobile out at the dump in Frederiksholm.* That doesn't sound that good, but in reality it was an excellent spot, in any case when the wind was blowing in the right direction. But then one evening when I came home, there was someone in the crate. I could tell by their voices that it was a man and a girl. Since at first I thought that they'd gone in there to be alone and that maybe it wouldn't take that long, I sat down to wait, because why shouldn't people be allowed to love each other even if they don't have a villa on the Coastal Road.* But when it'd gotten toward two o'clock and it'd gotten completely quiet in the crate, I went into it. It was very cold to be sitting outside for a long time and my feet were sore and swollen from tramping around all day. When I struck a match, I could see that they were lying over in the corner on my horse blanket. In spite of the cold, the girl was totally naked. I've had a good upbringing and left the crate and began to clear my throat. Completely without any effect. If I was going to rescue my little home, I was going to have to forget my good upbringing and get tough. Once again I made my entry into the crate, this time very noisily. Then both of them woke up and sat up and glared at me. In the flickering light of the match the girl was so beautiful a sight that my heart began pounding and my body remembered how long it'd been since I'd slept with a girl.

There was only one thing for me to do—make an awful fuss about finding uninvited guests in my crate. And I did that. I groused terribly and asked what the hell they thought they were doing and so on. That was the only tactic to be used in that situation and it failed. The man flew at my head, smashed my glasses, and threw me out of my own crate.

Toward morning I reached the horse stable on Larsbjørn Lane,* but it was so stuffed with homeless people that I couldn't find room and had to walk the streets until the people's kitchen* opened.

I'm a man in my early thirties. I came into the world in a nice home and got a nice upbringing. I'm neither an invalid nor mentally retarded; apart from my near-sightedness I'm really nicely endowed by nature. Like the ordinary run of people no doubt. And nevertheless I'm sitting here telling you my life story for a cup of coffee and money for a night's lodging. If you're expecting to hear something sensational, something adventurous, you're going to be disappointed—immorality and breaches of the law are some of the most unromantic things on this earth.

Now the manager's standing over by the cash register fuming that he can't throw me out for the time being. It's a shame he has to miss out on that pleasure. Life's so lacking in pleasures.

I don't know whether I said that my father was a parish deacon. He was. I grew up in a nice decent home. When I was fifteen years old, I ran away from home. I stole a bike and rode to Humlebæk,* where I stole a boat and sailed to Sweden. It wasn't especially romantic, unless it's romantic to freeze, starve, and be afraid. In Sweden I begged my way along the highways. One evening I came to a manor in Halland.* I'd walked a very long way without seeing a farm or a house that seemed to say *Welcome, come in and have a sandwich, drink a cup of coffee in my cozy kitchen, stay here tonight if you're too tired to keep walking*—or whatever a friendly facade of a house like that says to a fifteen-year-old vagabond trudging past out on the road. I suppose there'd been a couple of farms, but they were located so far from the main road that it wasn't worth the trouble, and the couple of humble houses I went past looked unsympathetic and had dogs that made a racket long before you got close to them.

Dogs are great judges of human beings. A constable riding by on a bicycle can stare at you speculatively and be in doubt as to your right to be walking on the road, and you can trick him by looking frank—a dog smells from a great distance that you're a vagabond. You can't trick him with a frank look, and the only way to avoid his teeth is to look rigidly ahead and walk by as if you hadn't at all noticed that a house was standing there. Besides, what would you want in a house whose inhabitants look at things in such a way that they'd get themselves a fierce cur.

My clothes were no longer in decent shape. In Ängelholm* I'd exchanged my shoes for a pair of canvas shoes. For the crown* I got in exchange I spent the night in lodgings for travellers.* My pants hung in shreds at the bottom and I hadn't changed underwear in a month. Just as the sun was going down, I came to a turn in the road where I had to go across a little bridge. I suppose the place was idyllic: a little church sat there on a hill, and tall poplars stood around a peaceful village pond. I was very tired and hungry.

A collection of barracks was located a little past the church. It was a quiet evening. I came to a crowd of day laborers; most of them were Poles.* A black-haired girl, who was sitting on the grass by the roadside, looked at me with a beautiful, calm look. She had a gaily colored scarf around her head and small, delicate gold rings in her ears.

The men said that if I felt like working in the beet fields, I could go up to the farmhouse and talk to the manager. They sized me up as being able to earn a few crowns a day on a piece rate, and for the time it lasted, I'd get shelter and a daily jug of milk. In addition, I could get as many potatoes as I wanted, but that really didn't mean that much—they'd sprouted and practically couldn't be eaten.

I went up to the farmhouse to talk to the manager. At the end of a tree-lined walk I came to a wrought-iron gate. Just inside in the garden there was a lawn where some children and a young girl were playing croquet. When I stopped to watch them, the young girl asked me angrily what I wanted. Was there any work in the beet fields on the farm? Work in the beet fields, she repeated, as if she'd never ever heard before that there was something called work in the beet fields. One of the children all of a sudden enthusiastically caught sight of me and said that I was certainly a *luffare*,* a beggar. Come Ysra, look, he's a real *luffare*.

In the middle of all that a man in tall riding boots came and asked in a brusque tone what I was doing in the garden. When I said I was looking for work in the beet fields, he looked at me disapprovingly and said that kind of thing took place on the farmstead.*

On the farmstead I found the manager, who was a friendly man. You could tell by looking at him that he himself took part in the work. While I was talking to him, the young girl who'd been playing croquet with the children came. During their conversation they moved a little bit away from me, but I still couldn't help hearing that it was me they were talking about. I heard her use expressions such as *people like that who come by road* and so on, and understood that for one reason or another she didn't like me getting the job.

But I got it anyway. The manager sent a boy with me down to the barracks to give instructions to assign lodging to me. As I left, I gave the young girl a triumphant look, but she didn't seem to notice. Had I known what awaited me, I wouldn't have taken the job that evening, but instead would've gone on and spent the night in some haystack or other in a field.

Do you know what a Copenhagen basement wash house* looks like? It's an elegant and cozy place in comparison to the room I was assigned in the barracks. The floor was cement, but too much sand had been put into the cement so that it crumbled when you just touched it. There were big holes in the floors with puddles of water; there was a rusty iron bed without bedding or mattress; a little rusty tiled stove without a door; and a hoeing apparatus that'd been put in here to be out of the way. The panes that were missing in the window had been replaced with margarine vat lids and tin advertisements for van Houten's cocoa.

4

When you're sitting like this at a people's kitchen gloriously aware that the manager can't come and chuck you out into the cold snow, that you've got money for a night's lodging, so you don't need to walk the streets at night, and still so much left over that morning coffee and cigarettes are taken care of, life seems quite pleasant to you after all. Then of course you've got all day long tomorrow to get the little bit of food you have to have and the couple of cents needed to get into bed. You totally forget how many times you failed to do it, how many nights you trudged up the street and down the street with an empty stomach, forget how you hated the well-fed idiots who were half-drunk on the way home from a binge and answered a polite request with a bad joke or flippant grin, forget that zealous police chased you away from the trolley waiting benches at City Hall Square, where there was after all a little shelter from the cold and you could rest your tired feet.

Humans have a wonderful ability to adapt. Up in a big office near City Hall Square there's a well-known man sitting with titles and status. There are nice things about him in Who's Who, and if he succeeds in kicking the bucket before the crash, he'll get a nice obituary. With the embezzlement he's committed there'd have to be a miracle to avoid the crash. Maybe he can manage for another year, maybe two. He's wishing that the world'll come to an end before that time, that war'll break out or something else catastrophic. He's not having a good time. And still he's assured in any event of one year. Nice villa, presentable car, sweet wife, amusements, and good food. Things are damn awful for him and twice a week he ponders suicide. I'm only assured of lodging for tonight plus coffee in the morning and cigarettes, but still I'm sitting here feeling a kind of pleasure in life. That evening on the Swedish manor I didn't feel especially happy about life. For some stupid reason or other I let myself be deprived of my freedom, agreed to root about in a beet field from sunup to sunset instead of wandering free as a bird down the highway, agreed to exchange my bed for the night in some haystack or other for a rusty iron bed in a foul-smelling barracks. My clothes didn't look so pretty to begin with, but what would they look like after I'd weeded beets for a week or so. I agreed to let myself be ordered about, to let myself be treated like a dog, and I did it completely voluntarily. It must be my good upbringing that was responsible for my not being able to say no when I was offered work.

I dragged the hoe out and tried to sweep the water up out of the puddles on the cement floor with an old sack that was lying in one corner. The only thing I accomplished was to get it spread across the floor. When I was finished with it, I was standing still in the middle of the room and was at my wits' end, standing and looking at the iron bed and pondering whether they'd expected me to sleep there without mattress or bedding. Or whether maybe they'd expected that I'd brought it along under my arm. I went outside to find someone who could help me solve this problem. The sun had set and the day laborers were settling down for the night; a bus drove by on the road. The sky was bright. It was very quiet and a white veil of bog mist lay down across the rush-grown stretch behind the village pond and the poplars. The air was spicy, far off there was someone laughing; the leaves of the poplars trembled. I cursed myself for having renounced my freedom.

Somebody was calling me from a window. It was the black-haired girl with the gold earrings. Did you eat, she asked. If I hadn't, I could eat with her and her sister. She was the one who'd looked at me with that beautiful gaze. After we'd eaten, the sister left and the girl with the earrings said there was no sense in thinking about managing to put together a bed on the iron monstrosity in my room, but instead I could sleep in her sister's bed since she was spending the night at her boyfriend's in the barracks next door. After I'd gone to bed, she took my socks and my shirt and went outside and washed them. I could hear the water bubbling in the bucket and that she was humming. I was very sleepy and was already dozing. When she came back in, she said that her name was Siska and that my clothes would be dry by the time I had to get up. Her name was actually Franciska, but they all said Siska because it was easier. I shouldn't misunderstand her doing something for me, she said—it was a pleasure for her. Then she turned out the light and went to bed.

5

Right after Siska'd turned off the light, I couldn't see anything at all, but could both hear and sense that she was pulling her dress over her head. Before she'd put it down, my eyes had become accustomed to the dark and I quite clearly saw her take off her slip. When she said good night, my heart was beating so fast I couldn't answer. She probably thought I was sleeping and finished undressing. In the summer night twilight her skin shone white—she was standing only a few steps from me. The gold earrings glinted whenever she moved, which accentuated her nakedness.

Even after she'd gone to bed, my heart wouldn't start functioning normally, and in spite of my being tired, it wasn't possible to fall asleep. My natural impulse of course was to get up and go over to her bed and, without further ado, lie down with her. But just the thought of making a movement was absurd; it was as if my limbs were stiff—I'd never have been able to pull it off; it would never've been possible to walk the few yards across the floor; I'd never ever get over there, even if I'd succeeded in getting up from the bed. Theoretically it would've been exceedingly easy. You just put one foot in front of the other, after that the other in front of the first, and in that way sooner or later reach her bed, where you just lift the blanket and very quietly lie down beside her. Theoretically it was exceedingly easy, but in practice it wasn't possible to move so much as a pinky.

Besides, she'd undoubtedly get angry about someone's having rewarded her kindness that way. Hadn't she in fact said that I shouldn't misunderstand her hospitality. If I hadn't had a good upbringing, it's possible that I'd have overcome my scruples. My father the parish deacon must've exulted in his heaven when he saw that I not only rejected sin, but that I was quite simply incapable of committing it.

6

Naturally it turned out that I couldn't keep up in the beets. The Poles would take two rows while I took one despite Siska's helping me. When she caught up with me, she'd cross over into my row and take a part of it before continuing in her own. When she reached the end of her row, she'd continue with mine till we met. She walked bent over with a small, short iron hoe. When I completely caught up with her, I could see down into her neck-line: she had buxom, round breasts, which shone white down in the dark. I longed for this moment.

It was hard work. And it was especially hard when you weren't used to it. When evening came, my back ached so I could only think about getting to lie down. Just as soon as I'd eaten, I went to bed, and despite my having dreamt all day long about the moment Siska went to bed, I was sleeping like a rock before the sun set.

The next day was Sunday. I awoke early, but Siska was already up. She was in a flowery kimono and had high-heel house slippers on her bare feet. Who'd have believed it. She was in fact a different woman. I was used to seeing her barefoot or with wooden shoes and wearing a coarse cotton dress, which was tucked up to her knees when she was in the field. Especially the high-heel slippers changed her, made her instep slimmer and her calf rounder.* Besides, they gave her a different posture, a more seductive one. But maybe it was the kimono. She'd done her hair carefully; women, I suppose, love to go around like that Sunday mornings pottering, dolling themselves up, and making themselves beautiful; her black hair lay like a frame around her delicate face with its black eyes.

When she saw I'd woken up, she said I should stay in bed—then I'd get coffee in bed. I couldn't take my eyes off her. She made the coffee on the portable kerosene stove, set the table, and dragged it over to my bed. After we'd drunk it, she fetched cigarettes and sat down on the edge of my bed and said I was a silly boy.

We smoked for a bit in silence. I felt terribly foolish and

awkward. Naturally she expected me to say something. And if I didn't say anything, maybe she'd realize how things stood with me and get offended by the fact that she couldn't sit on the edge of my bed without my having impure thoughts. Maybe she'd get so angry that I wouldn't be allowed to sleep there anymore, but would have to go back to the dismal barracks room with the tin ads and rusty iron bed. When she said I was missing a button on my neckband, I blushed. She let her hand stay on my neck and bent down over me and kissed me. When she made that movement, her belt flew open—she was naked underneath her kimono. The eternal laws of nature began to function: my hand was darting wildly, she lifted the blanket and her whole scent, warmth, and softness gushed forth over me. What would my father the parish deacon have said?

After breakfast we went on an outing. She put coffee in a beer bottle and packed it in a newspaper, buttered a couple of pieces of bread, and put the whole thing in a box made of vulcanized fiber, just like the ones the farm laborers have their breakfast in. It came with a strap so you could carry it. When we passed a crowd of day laborers at the end of the barracks, one of them made a comment. She just laughed and said I shouldn't pay attention to it.

We had a wonderful afternoon, which would've been perfect if we'd avoided a little experience that cast a tinge of bad feeling over the rest of the day. We'd lain down on a grassy slope out toward a forest road to drink coffee. Siska was frolicsome and fooled and larked about while laying the table on the grass. We played husband and wife, or rather, she did. She said that there was a red scarf at the merchant's that she'd so terribly much like to have—please let me buy it. I went along with the game and said it was out of the question as long as we hadn't paid the gas bill and that she was ruining me with her vanity. She said I was a brute of a man, who drank till I was juiced and went to bed with every girl in the world, but would begrudge his little wife a measly scarf, and asked if perhaps I meant to hit her if she bought it anyway. I confirmed it and tried to look very masculine and brutish. With a whip, she asked. Yeah, with a whip, I replied with my lower jaw jutting out, took her hard by the wrist, and twisted it around so she wound up lying down. So maybe you'll behave decently, I said. Yes, she whimpered and looked at me with her eyes enraptured. She was lying and fondling my hand, and said that I was so crude, but that she'd definitely be decent and never be disobedient. It was really funny, but very exasperating, and if just then I hadn't heard the tramp of horses, presumably I would've played the role to the end in keeping with her wish and in the midst of her mild protests and whimpering accusations of brutality.

But I did hear the tramp of horses. Siska straightened out her clothes, which had gotten mussed up, and we sat up since people are always ready to believe the worst. Before Siska'd managed to hook her dress at the neck, the rider had become visible in the bend in the road. It was the young girl who'd been playing croquet with the estate owner's children that evening I was looking for work. She slowly trotted past us with a bitter, spiteful look. Without greeting us. Siska said it was the governess up in the farmhouse, the one who was engaged to the manager. Her name was Miss Klara and the day laborers said she liked women. Yeah, but then how can she be engaged to the manager, I asked. Siska couldn't really understand that either, but she nevertheless didn't want to get into that subject any further.

The way Miss Klara had looked at us ruined the mood. Mine in any case. Siska tried to resume the game from before, but I couldn't forget the cold blue eyes and a short time afterward we left and set out on the way home. Two days later those blue eyes crossed my path again, this time with a more catastrophic effect.

7

It was right after quitting time that it began. I was standing and washing myself with a bucket outside the barracks. I'd taken off my shirt, was washing the whole upper part of my body, gargling, and was in a splendid mood, was standing and singing to myself during the whole cleaning festival—life was lovely. Siska was lovely, the manual labor did me good—I felt like doing gymnastics from a sheer sense of vitality.

I say that I felt like it. Of course I didn't do it. By nature I'm a calm and quiet person who can't stand attracting attention or doing anything violent; I've been brought up not to make noise or make a hullabaloo in any other way. Maybe that's why I sometimes get such a violent urge to shout and scream and do somersaults. By the way, it may well be that it was that urge that made me run away from home.

So I was standing and gargling when one of the girls from up in the farmhouse came and asked if I was the little Dane who'd come during the past week. I covered my naked upper body with the towel and said yes I was. I was supposed to go up to the farmhouse just as soon as I'd eaten, she said. I was supposed to be registered.* I was just supposed to go into the office—it was in the main building just to the right of the entrance.

That evening Siska was going to the dance at the inn together with her sister, and this way I had an excuse for not going along to the dance. I hate going to dances; I blush about everything, and when I have to walk across the floor to bow and ask a girl for a dance, I'm afraid of stumbling over my own feet and am certain that all the people are looking at me and smirking at me. So that worked out splendidly and after we'd eaten, I went up to the farmhouse.

When I knocked on the door to the office, nobody answered. I opened the door, went in, and cleared my throat. I made sure to stand out in the middle of the floor so that if the manager came he wouldn't think that I'd stolen something or been snooping in his things. It's a nasty feeling to be standing in other people's preserves waiting for their surprise at finding a stranger there. Especially for a vagabond who's come straight from the highway and gotten work. It's okay to regard people whose labor is poorly paid as criminals even before knowing them. There was a door besides the one I'd come in through. I went over and discretely knocked on it; people who weed beets need to be polite and modest. Still not a sound. I knocked harder.

This time somebody said *come in.* I opened the door with the slowness that's supposed to express deference.

I looked into a kind of study. There were big buffalo leather chairs, antlers on the walls, hunting implements, and all that kind of stuff; yes, there was also a picture of a naked girl in a forest—that's a funny thing, but you see that kind of picture so often even though in fact you never meet naked girls in the forest; I'm certain that there's never been anyone who's had that experience, even if they've lived their whole lives in the forests. That must be a kind of dream that people go around having. Or maybe it's because that way they can have a picture of a naked girl to go and look at without the parish church council's* getting offended. If it's art, there's of course nobody who'll dare say anything, except maybe just the most fanatic people of all. And damn it, they themselves have got their French pictures well locked up down in a drawer.

But there was no one in the room. On the other hand, there was a door open into another room—it must've been from there that somebody had said *come in.* I walked diagonally across the floor and knocked on the door frame. The farther you penetrate into the bigwigs' inner sanctum, the more discrete you have to be. And what a big chasm there is between a beet worker and an estate owner.

Someone got up in the room and appeared in the doorway. It was Miss Klara. She was in riding breeches, tall boots, and had a kind of silk shirt on. With a tie. She was erect and blond and looked straight at me with her blue eyes. Sort of a bit mockingly. It struck me that she was Siska's diametrical opposite, but that in one way or another they had something in common.

Oh, it's you, she said. Yes, we were of course supposed to have registered you—please come in.

She began to interrogate me in a very general way. What my name was, how old I was. Where I was from. Whether I had any papers. How it came about that I was going around begging on the highways in Sweden. In general I answered in conformity with the truth; I just didn't say that my father was a parish deacon, but rather that he'd died when I was little.

Suddenly she asked me to my great surprise whether I understood why she'd opposed my getting the job. She said it very vehemently and came all the way over to me. I couldn't make heads or tails of it and didn't know what to answer. She was standing and smiling in a strange way right into my face. I thought it was an evil smile.

I'm pretty sure I thought she was insane. In any case, I was so scared I didn't dare move. I didn't dare move so much as a finger. I think she stood there for several minutes with that strange, quivering, mocking smile without saying anything. As if she wanted to hypnotize me. As if she didn't dare say anything so I wouldn't wake up and go my way. Suddenly I noticed her hand touching mine very lightly. It was trembling and moist and hot. Then she whispered in a voice quivering with agitation: *You're such a girl*.

I was unspeakably afraid. Her hand was squeezing mine in an overwrought way and she was breathing heavily. She drew me to herself and kissed me with hard and burning dry lips, pressed her knee in between mine, took me and whispered spasmodically and indistinctly that I was a girl and that she was going to whip me to death. Now there was no longer any doubt that she was insane; I tore myself loose and darted out the door between the study and the office and out into the garden.

Second Chapter

1

I ran through the garden and didn't stop till I got to the wrought-iron gate. I mean, I might run into someone and it would look strange if I came dashing down through the tree-lined walk as if the devil were on my heels. I was certain that by fleeing I'd been saved from something terrible without actually making clear to myself what this terrible thing consisted of. It was certainly my good moral upbringing that had warned me at the last moment.

When I got down to the barracks, I began to feel that I'd behaved childishly and ridiculously. Maybe it was just Miss Klara's practical joke and I'd made a fool of myself. If I hadn't been so disheartened and well-mannered, the situation never would've arisen. And if I hadn't been brought up on such a horror of everything that couldn't be regarded as normal and decent, I wouldn't have behaved so foolishly. On a small scale I've never been afraid of doing what was forbidden; I've always been able, so to speak, to give vent to everything that was in me by pilfering and fibbing, but as soon as things took on a larger scale, I was gripped by panic and couldn't go through with anything.

I wouldn't have needed to be sitting here this evening and begging you for a cup of coffee and a night's lodging if I'd had the ability to take those chances life's given me. I'm going to tell you about my life lock, stock, and barrel. You'll get to hear some strange things. Maybe not what's romantic in the usual sense, but in any case the pure, sheer truth about a person who had a good upbringing and didn't amount to anything.

When I went into Siska's room, I suddenly felt like confiding the whole thing to her. I wanted to go up to the inn. True, I didn't have any money, but Siska had said that if I felt like going up there after I'd been at the farmhouse, I could just take a seat in the tap-room and order a beer—she'd pay all right.

The inn was jam packed with people. Both outdoors and indoors. Drunken and stark-raving mad people. Incessant traffic in and out the door. And as background for the whole din the dance music from the dance hall, which led out to the garden. I couldn't see Siska anywhere and that's why I went into the tap-room where I was so lucky as to find a place to sit, because there was just then a brawl and the two people who'd gotten into an altercation agreed to settle matters outside, where there was more room. After I'd been sitting for a bit waiting for my beer, one of the day laborers came along, a little tubercular Swede, and said that the manager had been there and asked if anyone'd seen me—he'd looked very worked up.

I became nervous about what the whole thing might turn into and didn't dare keep sitting there. I couldn't find Siska; I was in the dance hall, through the whole tap-room, and all around the whole building. Finally I went out into the garden—it was a very trampled garden with some shrubbery and home-made benches. In all corners where there was a little bit of darkness you could hear voices whispering or see the vague outline of couples making love. Behind the inn garden there was a little grove of birch trees and alders. If that's the way things looked in the inn garden, what must they have looked like in the grove? And besides, it was so dark I wouldn't be able to see her; it was better if I went back to the tap-room. On the way in I ran into her. She was together with one of the hands from up at the farm house. I felt very relieved and was glad to see that she didn't look so heated up and that her dress wasn't wrinkled like many of the other girls'. I said to her that I wanted to talk to her and we went outside a little piece away from the road and sat down at the edge of a ditch. It was very mild and the mosquitoes almost wouldn't leave us alone; the noise from up at the inn sounded as if it came from a lunatic asylum where the patients had revolted; out here it was tranquil—you could hear the little sounds of the roadside. There was a scent of the newly mowed hay from the field behind us.

I told Siska the whole story, even the business about the manager who was going around looking for me and looked so crazy. She sat for a bit and thought it over and then said that you never knew what might come of it; it was probably better that I go away this very evening—there was a bus that went to town at

11:30. She wanted to give me ten crowns; maybe I could get some work in town, maybe there was a ship in the harbor where I could sign on—in Halmstad* there were many ships. Otherwise I could go to Falkenberg* and try there.

We sat for some time without saying anything. I was sorry about having to leave her and said that we'd write to each other. She thought that was a bunch of nonsense. But maybe we'll never see each other again, I said. She looked at me surprised—of course we wouldn't. That'd certainly be a strange coincidence. I was pained by the fact that she could take it so coolly and I took her hand. But now she became impatient and wanted to go back to the dance; she gave me a hurried kiss and got up, laughed a bit at my sadness and said that I was a silly boy and that she'd surely think about me sometimes.

2

In Halmstad I found out that the town was hot right then. That is, that the police were conducting round-ups of vagabonds. There was a big dispute over the cause: some said that it was because we'd now gotten to that time of year when the officers went around being bored—it'd become too warm to sit indoors playing cards and it wasn't warm enough yet to go spy on lovers in the park down by the river. Some said that it was because the chief of police was seeking a transfer to a town known for its aversion to tramps and that he now wanted to document that he was capable of keeping the riff-raff away.

I of course couldn't have cared less what the cause was—I didn't feel like being sent home to the saying of grace and potted plants and that's why I immediately left this inhospitable town to go to Falkenberg. On the way I joined company with an old beachcomber* who was so fat that he had a hard time begging clothes that fit him. On the other hand, he always got first-class clothes whenever he finally got some. He took only the same size clothes as clergymen and bank presidents and didn't know what it meant to go around in ready-made clothes. The size alone meant that it had to be tailored.

In Falkenberg I lived at Mother Britta's. She's an old woman who lives from housing traveling journeymen, or lived, because she's probably dead now. The thing was that her house was located just outside the city limits so Falkenberg's police had no business there, and the *luffer* were freed from reporting their arrival and departure* and all that stuff that people who take to the road hate, not always because they don't have a clear conscience, but because they're anarchists. That doesn't mean that they're adherents of a definite political idea—they don't give a damn about all that; it's their temperament that's anarchistic. And at Mother Britta's they could be left alone by the Falkenberg police,* who carried sabers and only got a chance to show their stuff when there was a fair in town. Mother Britta never asked for identification or anything like that; she asked if you had lice, and when you'd said no and paid fifty øre, you were assured of lodging for the night. Actually it was odd that she asked about that—I can hardly imagine that there was ever anyone who said yes. And all of them had lice—they called them *spikes**—and joked about hating to have their blood mixed. There's a story that there was supposed to be a race in Norrland* that consisted of some big fellas with a cross on their backs. But that was doubtless a lie; at least I've never seen any such guys.

Mother Britta had about ten house guests divided between two rooms. Apart from an itinerant girl, who slept in Mother Britta's room. She was a tall, thin beanpole, who made some sort of thigamajigs out of bits of rope to put combs in; she unraveled the piece of rope so it resembled hair that had been let down, and tied a red silk ribbon around one end. It looked really attractive. The farm girls were delighted with them and I'm pretty sure the girl earned good money. The ten guests represented just as many kinds of vagabonds. There were *broad-gaugers*—they were the ones who calmly and level-headedly tramped along the highways and took life's goods in the order in which they came without trying to interfere with their fate by making drastic decisions; then there were the *tap dancers*, who didn't give a damn about the open country and only cared about the towns—they travelled by train as stowaways or stopped cars on the highways and were allowed to hitch a ride, or they quite simply paid for their railway ticket: it could be worth it—they polished off a town in the course of a couple of days and didn't feel like hanging around and wasting time on the highway.

Then there were the *hawkers*.* They dealt in one thing or another, shoelaces, shoe polish, soap, postcards, safety pins, and all that kind of stuff. They were business people and they seldom mixed with a broad-gauger; in a pinch they might permit themselves to discuss the cities' heat with a tap-dancer.

I was brought up well and have honest social ambitions.* Or rather had. In the course of two weeks I'd run through the various stages and become a hawker. I'd come to town as a broad-gauger, but quickly discovered that it paid to take the bus out to the small communities* in the vicinity and beg there instead of in Falkenberg, where you could run around all day to scrape together a dollar.* The communities weren't so overrun—you could easily take home several crowns without having over-exerted yourself especially. One evening one of the hawkers asked me whether I'd buy a bunch of safety pins from him since he'd gotten a job as an agent for selling lace to private customers. I bought them and began doing business. It was in all respects progress: I earned more and more easily, it was less risky and more pleasant. I had to laugh when I thought about what a beet worker had to do to earn a day wage that was less than mine.

3

The beggars' hotel's bourgeoisie consisted of two hawkers, the tall thin girl, a nationally known vagabond named Värmlands-Kalle,* and me. I was included because I was so young and because I was a Dane. The exotic and the uncommon are highly valued. Meanwhile it was Easter and the bourgeoisie had decided to celebrate Easter on Sunday. We chipped in and went shopping. The main components of the feast were macaroni, boiled eggs, and liquor. Lots of liquor. The beanpole arranged the meal. Mother Britta was the guest of honor and handed out cigars for this occasion. It started off in an unusually nice and bourgeois way. There was a white cloth on the table and three daffodils in a glass. We enjoyed behaving nicely and feeling like burghers. We ate in a cultivated way. Even Värmlands-Kalle ate in a cultivated way.

We'd bought three times as many eggs as we could eat. On the other hand, the liquor ran out before we got to the coffee. We chipped in again and bought a new supply from Mother Britta. Before I got drunk for real, I remember that Kalle was sitting and telling funny stories. He was a specialist, dealt in French pictures and condoms, and supplemented his business with small-time swindling. He used two boxes of snuff a day and was missing two fingers on his left hand. The beanpole had become sentimental, she was sitting and blathering on about a walk in the woods where she'd gone with her betrothed holding hands, and saying something about nightingales, the wonders of love, and all that kind of stuff. One of the hawkers was infected by her sentimentality and together they left the party to devote themselves to these subjects in peace.

After I'd thrown up down in the garden, I was put to bed. Mother Britta took my clothes off with her own hands; she was an ugly old hag all right, but she was a good person. In the evening she brought in a glass of milk, and after I'd drunk it, I wasn't so ill that I couldn't go for a walk.

When I walked down across the market place, I saw that a circus had come to town; a lot of people were standing and watching the tents being raised. Damn it, they had to do a bunch of work, those circus people. When you see someone like a jockey in the ring, you don't think about the fact that at one and the same time he's a laborer and has to pitch in with the heavy drudge work, that he's a laborer, groom, and transport worker.

I joined the spectators—it's always nice to see people doing some work. In spite of the liquor-breakfast I felt fit, but felt like smoking a cigarette. There was a farm boy standing next to me who'd just lit one, revealing that he had a whole pack. But it was *Bridge*, and I didn't much care to smoke Bridge, which isn't a good cigarette. A well-dressed youth was standing a little farther on who looked as though he might well smoke a decent brand. I ingratiated myself with him* and when I saw that he was smoking *SSS*, I asked if I might take one along for my buddy too. Later I saw all right that he noticed that I was alone and that that business with the buddy was a scam, but of course he could hardly come over and demand the other one back.

When I'd seen my fill of the circus crew, I took a walk down to the river. My stomach felt a bit empty and I went into a villa and asked for a sandwich. The maid was home alone and I was seated in the kitchen and I got both coffee and a cigar after the meal. Before I was done, the master and mistress came home, and the maid let me into her room so as not to have any trouble with the wife.

I sat for an hour and a half on the maid's bed and couldn't get out. One of the beanpole's comb-holders, an amateur picture of a marine with a beard, and a picture of Christ were hanging on the wall. A wall rug hung over the couch with an embroidered inscription: Your own home is worth its weight in gold.

In addition, a couple of darned stockings were hanging over the back of a chair. Spilled powder was on the table. And an English textbook was lying there.

When the maid finally came back, she gave me fifty øre, a pair of her master's socks, and a scriptural passage. I said that I'd wait to change socks till I got home. She asked where I was living, and when I told her, she looked very worried. A little later she asked whether I was saved. I didn't really know what to answer, but I said that my father was a parish deacon. That seemed to do, but appeared to disappoint her a bit, since she'd doubtless been dreaming of eventually saving someone or other. She let me out through the garden.

4

A Thurø-schooner is a schooner that's native to Thurø.* But

it's not just the ship's construction and its place of origin that differentiates it from other sailing ships. In a way, there'd be no need for bearing a designation of its domicile; everybody who's had a little to do with ships would be able to say right away what kind of craft it was. For that matter, the craft could disguise itself and the skipper assume a Dutch name—that wouldn't help a bit: it'd inevitably be brought to light that it was a Thurø-schooner. The ship's atmosphere would betray it; the thickest paint wouldn't be able to cover the vapor of Funen petty-bourgeoisdom. And if you didn't have a sense of smell for that kind of thing, the food and discipline would tell you that, all right.

When I left the maid, who'd given me a pair of her master's socks and a scriptural passage, I didn't know anything about Thurø-schooners. Didn't know anything about ships at all. Before twelve hours had passed, I knew what a Thurø-schooner was, but by then it was too late—the "Constantia" was out on the Kattegat's wild waves, and I wouldn't have been able to slip back onto land anyway.

Of course, I ought to have become suspicious right away when the man I got to chatting with down at the harbor told me that there was a Danish ship there the crew had deserted. Crews really don't desert just like that for the fun of it. They desert because there's something wrong with the conditions on board. In reality, it's totally idiotic for the police to arrest sailors who've deserted and haul them before a judge who imposes harsh sentences on them. Of course, it was the skipper who should be brought before the court and account for the abuses and promise the judge to mend his ways. But if that still hasn't dawned on the courts, maybe I can be excused for not having realized it either and not having figured out right away that, if the crew of the "Constantia" deserted, it was because it wasn't a pleasant ship to sail on.

The way things now stood, I was inclined to believe that the skipper was right when he said that they were a bunch of damned dirty swine who hadn't earned their keep and that in reality he was ecstatic over having gotten rid of them. Could I be the cook? I certainly thought I could. That suited him fine—then he'd get off with just telegraphing for two ordinary seamen.* So that matter was settled; he was an open-minded man, the skipper—I had neither papers nor a discharge book.* I could stay on board right away; the two ordinary seamen were supposed to come the next morning from Copenhagen, and as soon as they came, we'd sail. He was so nice, the skipper, he gave me a crown and said that I could go up and have myself a drink at the cafe on the corner. The future looked bright and friendly for me: I'd get to see foreign countries and life on board would probably be enjoyable and romantic. The skipper was probably like a father to his people. Incomprehensible that those people had deserted. But if they were that stupid, they also didn't deserve anything better than to be arrested.

While sitting at the cafe, I already felt like an old seaman, and in relation to the landlubbers sitting in there, I felt a certain pride: I mean, now I was a son of the sea, actually I'd always been, I was born for the sea, had always loved life at sea, in school they'd called me seaman because I'd read a seaman's novel and taught myself to walk with the same rolling movements as sailors and use technical maritime terms the other students didn't understand. Besides, undoubtedly I had an innate aptitude for seamanship: it surely wasn't every fifteen-year-old boy who could sail a stolen one-masted skiff from Humlebæk to Sweden, was it? And when I thought back to that night, it actually seemed that there was a pretty good wind. It'd probably been what you call a strong breeze. Even old sailors would certainly have been astounded by the feat.

In any case, now I'd signed on as cook on the Thurø-schooner the "Constantia" and was sitting with my beer longing for a few breakers and a little whistling in the rigging. Damn it, that was something else than rooting around in a beet field, selling safety pins, or begging for a sandwich from some farmers who didn't know anything about the world except the ground they went clumping around on their whole lives. I bought myself one more beer and looked weather-beaten.

5

When the ordinary seamen came the next morning, we were towed out of the harbor and left to our fates. We had deck cargo. Mine timber. There was enough wind to fill the sails, the sky was blue, and a small archipelago of skerries* and a couple of gulls made the departure a perfect idyll. We calmly glided off and the skipper was standing astern looking congenial. Kind of a real Funen grandfather with a pointy beard and blue eyes. The ordinary seamen went around putting things straight on deck and the mate had turned in to sleep. I was sitting in the galley making preparations for lunch. Fruit soup* and hash.

Toward noon the skipper brought prunes and raisins for the soup. One prune and five raisins for each one. By now the coast had become a narrow strip and there weren't so many gulls. Here beyond the archipelago of skerries the boat was bobbing up and down a little; I could see that in the galley by the fact that the frying pan and pots that were hanging on the wall first slid slowly to one side, stopped there for a bit, and then slid slowly to the other side. I couldn't stand it. Especially not in connection with the smell of the food. A bucket of water was standing on the floor. It was only three-fourths full, but one second the water was about to run over the brim, then it stopped, sank slowly, and began to rise on the other side till it was about to run over there; a raisin that was lying on the table rolled back and forth at the same speed. From one end of the table to the other end of the table. I couldn't stand it. It was unpleasant. And all these movements were backed up by sounds that accentuated the rhythm. I dashed out to the railing and threw up. Naturally to the windward, where the wind struck the ship's side and sprayed the gall in my face.

It could've been worse. I went back to the galley, drank a little water, and ate a raisin. It was the one that had been lying on the table rolling back and forth.

The skipper had said that when they called *ready about*, I had to rush forward like a wild animal and loosen the foresail sheet, hold on tight, and let go only when the craft had turned so far that the wind no longer caught the sail. Then I had to jump over to the other side, haul taut and fasten it. Just as I'd finished eating the raisin, they shouted *ready about*. I immediately forgot my bad stomach and darted off. As I stood at my place by the foresail, I was proud of my job. For the first time in my life I felt the joy of being a real man. I stood with my legs far apart and held on to the sheet with both hands.

6

When I came back to the galley, it was full of soot and smoke. Everything was covered with greasy black specks. The food too. And new blasts of black clouds were coming out of the stove through hundreds of cracks.

Of course, I could figure out the cause, all right. The galley's chimney was an angular pipe made of tin; when the craft turned, the wind blew down into the pipe. In other words, it had to be turned in the direction of the wind every time we turned. I don't know whether I'd considered it, or maybe thought that it turned on its own. I mean, you could easily think that. Just like a weather vane, right? When I went out of the galley to crawl up on the roof and turn the chimney, I was black with soot all over. The mate was standing close by. He looked at me as if he were going to devour me and asked why damn it to hell I hadn't turned the flue. I said that I hadn't known that it had to be turned. Then maybe this here can help you remember, he said, and hit me with his fist below my ear so I went crashing down. That brutal animal. He wasn't even allowed to sail as a mate—the ordinary seamen said that he didn't have a certificate And the skipper only had a certificate for domestic shipping. Only had permission to sail in coastal trade. Damn it, this was some tub. If I hadn't had such a nice upbringing, I'd have said country bumpkin to him. To the mate, I mean.

I clambered up on to the galley and turned the flue. Afterward I tried to clean the galley and scrape the soot off the food. It was only somewhat successful.

A little before noon one of the ordinary seamen came to see what we were going to have for lunch. His name was Leo. A few years ago I read in the newspaper that he'd been knocked overboard by a breaker in the Mediterranean. That was on one of ØK's* ships. When he saw the mess, he asked whether I'd been a cook before. In order not to get into a row, I said I'd been a cook's apprentice in one of Stockholm's finest hotels for two years. He said that was a lie and wanted to know if I had a discharge book. I said I'd pawned it for a night's lodging at a hotel in Halmstad. Then he didn't want to ask anything else, but I could see by looking at him that he'd return to these questions another time.

7

We lay off Skagen* for three days and couldn't get any farther. The craft couldn't go close-hauled.* We were really moving fast— we weren't lying still; the craft rolled over the waves, but every three hours we got to the big buoy and hadn't gotten the slightest bit farther. We turned incessantly. I no longer thought it was such fun to deal with the foresail. We were going to the Faroe Islands, and if things kept up the way they had been, it could certainly take a while before we got up there.

When we finally got out into the North Sea, the seaman's proud and romantic life began for real. By now of course it was well into that time of year when the fall storms begin to entertain seamen. I was so sick that I no longer bothered to crawl to the railing—I was content with holding my head outside the galley door. Besides, my stomach was empty—I could only force a little bit of gall and some stomach cramps. I was completely sluggish, performed my work automatically, and took the drubbings I got without a murmur. I wasn't doing so well. There wasn't a mattress or blankets in my bunk, so I spent the nights in the canvas room where I rolled myself in a tarpaulin as well as could be done. It was prohibited, but the skipper and the mate never went into the crew cabin.

I really had enough to do: I cleaned, made beds, emptied spittoons, and cooked. The ordinary seamen were nice to me, begged for extra coffee, and bad-mouthed the mate to please me. To please them, I stole from the provisions astern and from the skipper's booze. Myself, I lived on raisins and water.

One morning we saw several islands on the horizon. They resembled large grassy heaps lying about on the water. It was the Faroe Islands. They disappeared again from sight, we turned the craft, and a little later they reemerged, this time closer. Then night fell and when it became light again, we were lying quite near them, and a long narrow rowboat with long narrow oars was on the way out to us. The men in the boat had on funny little knitted caps and ox-hide shoes.* It was the pilot's boat. The pilot was the tall thin old fellow standing at the back of the boat, said Leo. When they reached us, the old man clambered up the ladder and went aft, where he took the tiller out of the skipper's hands without saying a word. He cast a skeptical sidelong glance up at the sails and shifted the tiller hard as if to show the skipper what a big idiot he was.

When we dropped anchor at Thorshavn* roads,* the mate said that I couldn't have permission to go on land. I went down and complained to the skipper, who set aside the ban and quarreled with the mate for an hour down in the cabin. The mate's name was Theobald Jensen. When he came up, he was white with rage and set me to scrubbing the galley so that in any event I wouldn't get too much enjoyment out of my visit on shore.

8

The mate hadn't had any need to be afraid. I didn't desert on the Faroe Islands. I mean, that would've been crazy. We unloaded some of the cargo in Thorshavn and got rid of the rest in Selletræ,* returned to Thorshavn with the dead freight, and loaded dried fish. One evening I went ashore with the two ordinary seamen: we went to the movies with three girls; it was

Leo who'd taken care that I also got a girl. Outside town there was something they called the woods; we went out there when we got out of the movies. It turned out to be a collection of small, low bushes. It was cold; Leo was far ahead with his girl; he talked nonstop and smoked one cigarette after the other. None of the rest of us said anything. I hardly dared look at my girl; she was a chubby little one, who was just as embarrassed as I myself was. When we reached the bushes, we stopped automatically. The sky was bright and cold, and there was something run-down and trampled about the low brush; all the small, narrow paths into the thicket made you depressed and uneasy.

Suddenly we were standing alone. The others had each found their path, but the chubby little girl and I stood there like two children life was now suddenly demanding something from, which accordingly had to be done, something that actually you'd love to do, but didn't really dare do. In any case, that's the way I felt.

I'd heard enough stories to know what I was supposed to do in such a situation, but I knew ahead of time that I couldn't pull it off. It was as if the stories got me more excited than reality. I mean, now I was in fact standing there in the situation that I'd so often visualized in my fantasy, and what I really felt like doing was running away from the whole thing. It was very awkward—what must the girl have thought of me. In any event, I had to do something. I happened to think of Siska—that was something totally different; with Siska there hadn't been any need for me to make a decision—it all went automatically. This girl expected me to do something.

I put my arm around her and kissed her. She immediately opened up like a flower and pressed herself up against me. I unbuttoned her coat. The rest of the story was ruined by the fact that I felt ludicrous because I lost my balance. When I again pressed her up against me and kissed her, my lips turned wet with her tears. We took each other's hand and walked back to town. She said that I should write her and asked whether I thought I'd be going to any interesting countries. Her brother collected stamps.

The dried fish were destined for Grimsby* in England. After we'd been at sea for a couple of days, it was brought to light that the ordinary seamen's love affairs had had consequences, so the skipper had to put on his glasses and get cracking with the thick physician's manual lying in his cabin. What does life have to offer a seaman. Even love is poisoned. Leo was stuffed to the gills with cheap cynicism and claimed you weren't a real man till you had such a bout. I was happy about having survived the trip to the woods so successfully and was glad to wait a bit yet to become a real man.

The ordinary seaman's bad luck gave the mate material for a bunch of impudent things, and one Sunday morning he and Leo were sprawled on the deck scuffling. By the way, it was a lovely calm morning, the sea was smooth as oil, and twice we'd seen a whale far off. We were going to have boiled beef for lunch; it was a pleasant change and easy to prepare. Naturally we lived mainly on dried fish—after all, it was free, you could just go get it from the cargo hold. The skipper didn't worry about its not being especially well suited for human consumption. During the scuffle the skipper kept below deck, but the rest of us were attentive spectators and were happy every time Leo's fist established contact with the mate's jaw. Finally the mate got hold of a spike and hit Leo hard above one eye so blood flowed down over his face.

Next day the wind rose and off the Orkney Islands* we got into violent weather. The cargo shifted and we listed. For several days we lay to* with sails reefed and waited for it to clear up. The waves washed over the deck and the storm made music in the rigging, so you couldn't hear your own voice even if you screamed at the top of your lungs. The ordinary seamen took turns turning the tiller; they were in oilskins and tall rubber boots; I had on the clothes I'd come on board in and was sopping wet from head to toe. It's incredible that I was able to stand it: other people get influenza from sitting on a bench at Langelinie pier* without a coat on an early spring day and some die from wet feet. In the afternoon that day the storm was at its high point and we thought the coast was getting closer and closer; the mate sent Leo up into the rigging to reef the sails. It sounded like a death sentence.

While Leo was up there, the skipper took the tiller and after that was over with, he took Leo along down astern and gave him a tin mug of cognac. At that time I felt that the whole world stood and fell with whether Leo returned alive down from the spar, but now after the fact I feel that, after all, in a way it didn't matter whether his existence had been brought to an end that afternoon in the North Sea or that night several years later in the Mediterranean when he was washed overboard.

10

When we got to Grimsby I deserted. I'd planned it before I'd seen the English coast and was just waiting for a suitable opportunity. We got into the dock in the evening, but couldn't berth alongside the wharf till the next morning. Late in the morning some brokers and such came on board and there was a terrible hullabaloo about the cargo, which had shifted and was partially ruined. The buyers refused to accept the fish, there was a lot of running about by a bunch of people, some of them were very worked up, and the skipper's face was like a thundercloud. Leo said the whole thing was a charade on the part of the agents to push down the price of the fish. Finally it was worked out and the unloading began later in the afternoon.

The fish was hauled up in baskets out of the cargo hold; a dozen girls and young women had come on board to put the fish in baskets. They immediately inundated the ship from front to stern, a couple of them sat down with me in the galley, made me blush at their vulgarities, and persuaded me to make coffee. Unfortunately, there was certainly no doubt that their crude advances were due to the coffee and not my person. Imagine what I looked like: I hadn't washed in the time we'd been at sea, my hair was long, I had on a tattered jacket that was stiff from scraps of food, soot, and other pleasant forms of dirt, my shirt was greyish-yellow and hadn't been off my body since I was in Falkenberg, but for all that my pants were the worst. Even an expert wouldn't have been able to say what material they were originally made of; one pants leg was torn and I had had to tie a piece of twine around my ankle to keep it together. One of the girls was good-looking: she was black-haired, had brown eyes, and was chock-full of charm and roguery; she had on an old washed-out silk blouse that sat tight around her breasts, and a sackcloth apron, that slid up when she sat down and showed her round, bare knees. She managed to persuade me to sneak aft and steal a bag of coffee for her from the skipper's cupboard.

11

After I'd washed up after dinner, I fetched a bucket of fresh water, heated up it on the stove, and took it down into the cabin where I cast off all my clothes and scrubbed myself with a wad of cotton waste and green soap from head to toe, made my hair sopping wet, and made an elegant part with the help of Leo's pocket mirror. When I came up on deck, the girls were knocking off, the ordinary seamen were putting on the hatches, which were full of salt and bits of dried fish everywhere, the skipper and the mate were below decks, the evening calm was beginning to settle over the dock; only over at the coal cranes, where work went on around the clock, was there a racket and rattling, which could be heard that much more strongly because of the beginning quiet. The girl with the round knees was standing on the wharf, she had the bag of coffee in her hand; out in life there were experiences and wonderful things—it was only on ships that life was depressing and meaningless. I'd fled from home to avoid rules and compulsion, but I was constantly getting involved in slavery again because I'd been raised to knuckle under to compulsion. But now that was going to be over with. The slavery was going to be over with. I'd desert this very evening.

I went down into the cabin and packed my things in a little

bundle; I left some postcards from the Faroe Islands and a picture of a Swedish film star there. When I came up again, the ordinary seamen were in the galley. Doubtless to drink coffee. I stuck the bundle under my jacket and left the "Constantia."

Third Chapter

1

When you're sitting like this at a people's kitchen and have to give an account of your life, you're inclined to forget what it actually is that you want. You're inclined to let yourself be carried away by what you've experienced and just talk away. Events and people surface; dramatic experiences that were actually insignificant are revived in your memory.

I mean, back then I didn't understand why I'd run away from home and why I behaved the way I did. And in a way, I probably don't understand it today either. Other people would presumably have experienced something completely different than I did. I mean, it's not so much what you get mixed up in as the way you face things that matters. I think it was my misfortune to have been brought up too respectably. Or too boringly. During all the time I roamed around Europe, even during the harshest periods, I never longed for home. The memories of my childhood home have always depressed me. The quiet living room, the rule-bound life, the newspaper holder with *Hovedstaden** and *Kristeligt Dagblad*,* where the papers from the day before were taken out every morning and put in the haybox, every morning on the dot, the calm ticking of the clock, the potted plants, and the picture of Jesus blessing the little children.

Sometimes I didn't have such a good time of it, I starved, and wasn't in a bed for weeks, but I never longed for the close, stagnant rooms where I lived in my childhood, never missed the cage of rules, laws, customs, and morality that secured its residents against life's dangers and insecurity, but at the same time removed every sensation of living. Everything was situated within fixed limits; you never needed to be in doubt about how you were supposed to act. You had the laws and rules to stick to. You had to do that and you weren't allowed to do this. And it was always the most interesting thing that was forbidden and the boring thing that you had to do.

I've experienced many strange and unusual things. Things

people in general don't meet up with. I've been a doorman in Paris, smuggler on the Norwegian-Swedish border, shoestring dealer in Hamburg, and tour guide on the Riviera. And, still, lying on the side of the road has been my greatest experience, lying there on my back just staring up into the air, being completely free and independent, completely without responsibility, without obligations. Freer than the birds, which have a nest and mate and chicks and all that stuff. Not having any domicile, any goal, was a splendid thing; lying on the outskirts of a forest a million miles from what's called civilization, lying there in a bed of bear skin fescue,* wild chervil, and forget-me-nots and counting yourself lucky that you're not standing in a factory or sitting in a galley.

There was just one thing I had to make sure of: scrupulously avoiding all work. The danger of getting work lurked everywhere you went; twice I'd let myself be tricked and sacrificed my freedom: I'd gone to work with a go-getter's impulse and zeal and experienced a miserable and fettered existence—all that stuff I'd run away from home to avoid. What pleasure is there in hoeing beets. What pleasure is there in being a messroom boy on a Thurø-schooner. You get a place to sleep and you get something to put in your stomach. But I mean, you get that anyway. And I've never had such bad bunks and never eaten so badly as when I let myself be lured into taking a job.

But it could be hard to avoid. People would try to lure you in every possible way. They used all the ploys. Some of them believed in the principle that if they gave you a little bit of food, in return you were supposed to do a little work, chop a little wood, do a bit in the garden or something like that. And if, based on your unfortunate upbringing, you were so stupid as to say yes, you might be at risk that they'd urge you to stay—they had a lot that had to be done; you could live up in the loft—you'd definitely get a little for it and so on. Or they'd heard that the farmer next door needed a young man and they absolutely wanted to go along with you over there and make sure you got the job.

The damn thing about it was that you were forced to pretend

that actually you'd love to have something to sink your teeth into, you were forced to bend over backwards agreeing with the whole thing and let yourself be hauled along to the farmer's and let yourself be hog-tied to a wheelbarrow and a shovel instead of going off on the tramp down the road free and easy. Otherwise you'd forfeit people's sympathy and get neither food nor money for lodging. People were peculiar on that point—they said that work ennobles and all that kind of stuff. The vagabonds said that work ennobles, but the nobility don't work. Besides, people always wanted to know what your profession was, and since you were forced to say something, I used to say I was a gardener's trainee. I felt that sounded nice. Especially that stuff about being a trainee. In other occupations the ones who went for the beer were just apprentices, but among the gardeners they were trainees. That was, so to speak, a bit superior. And when I went to places where there was a need for gardener's trainees, I immediately did an about-face and said I was a carpenter or whatever I could think of right then.

I went from Grimsby to Hamburg as a stowaway on an English freighter. It was a disgusting trip. To begin with, I walked around Grimsby for a couple of days and enjoyed the freedom I'd regained without actually knowing what to use it for. One night I sneaked on board one of The United's* boats, a butter boat*—I think it was called "Primula"*—to ask the crew for a little food. They said I was wanted for desertion and that I'd better try and get out of town one way or another; there was a freighter over by the coal cranes that was probably going to Hamburg.

Toward morning I boarded the freighter and hid in a lifeboat that was covered with canvas. In the boat there was a compass, a can of water, and a container with biscuits. After I'd been lying there freezing for two days and nights, we docked at Hamburg and when night fell, I left my hiding place and went ashore. That night and the next day I walked Hamburg's streets. The following night I slept in a little Scandinavian seaman's home on *Little Parrot Street** in Altona.* I had no money, but I pawned my bundle.

But I had to try and get out of Hamburg. After all, a city represented everything I wanted to avoid. The real freedom was on the highway. Wandering through beautiful landscapes completely free and independent. Mountains, forests, and lakes. Chirping birds and a brook trickling down the mountain, a grassy slope beside the brook where you could lie stretched out and loaf. Just as long as you cared to. Without anyone coming and asking why you were lounging about there. No need to jump up whenever someone came. And to stand looking embarrassed like a thief who's been caught red-handed. Just remain lying and stare up into the air. Nobody could boss you around. No obligations, none at all. No responsibility. Free and independent.

2

And if you got hungry, you just needed to go into a farmhouse and ask for a bite to eat. Everybody knows from films and tourist propaganda what such a German farm looks like. Well-kept half-timbered buildings, beautiful, sunburned people in national costumes, a cheerfully barking dog bids you welcome. On such a farm they'd receive a travelling journeyman in a friendly way, almost enthusiastically—it meant a diversion, a breath of air from the great wide world. You'd be entertained, persuaded to stay overnight.

In Sweden it'd been something else again. Sweden's so densely populated and so overrun with vagabonds. Here in Germany the farms were located so far apart from one another. And I'd certainly wind up experiencing something. The great experience lies in wait on the highway. Maybe I'd stop off in some idyllic little mountain village, take a job for a week or so, go for a stroll after knocking off for the day with the most beautiful girl in the field, maybe seduce her in the little grove by the brook. And I'd move on to new districts, new experiences, new adventures. That'd be the life. That's the way life was supposed to be lived.

That'd be something different than walking around in a

windy seaport like Hamburg tightening your belt, sleeping in a filthy seaman's home, where you'd be treated like a dog, and spending the day wandering around in cold and wet streets, hungry and homeless.

So out on to the highway. Hamburg was hell. Being without means in a city is to be the least advantaged person, to have the worst possible conditions for getting something to eat and a bed to sleep in. And if you finally do get any, it's the vilest grub and the most miserable lodging. Not having to work just means that you have nothing to do, that you feel superfluous, rejected; idleness is a curse—you saunter up and down the streets and don't know how to make time pass, you're treated like a dog by the police and meet with hostility from people. You constantly go around fearing arrest; if you're finally able to pay for lodging, you don't know whether it'll be the police that'll come to wake you; if you don't have lodging, you don't dare sit down on a bench to try to sleep a little—then the damn officers will come and want to hear a little about what kind a fella you are. Damn it, decent people can sit on the benches all night long, if they feel like it. And, after all, they have a warm bed they can go home to; it'd be more reasonable if you chased them away from the benches.

A city is hell for a person without money or without friends. There's nowhere you can feel as lonely as in a city; nowhere is the danger of having to stay overnight greater than there in the midst of all the houses. You aren't even allowed to go into a stairway; nowhere is the danger of winding up starving greater than where piles of foodstuffs are heaped up; nowhere do you feel lonelier than in the midst of a throng of people.

But out in the country it'll be something totally different again. There you'd surely also have a goal—getting from one place to the next; when, overcome by sensations and wandering, you lay down to sleep in the fragrant hay of some barn or other, you'd have the satisfaction of having gotten so far, maybe twenty miles, maybe thirty. And you wouldn't know what the next day would bring, what districts you'd get to, what experiences you'd be exposed to.

In the city one day was like the next. And every day felt as if it was wasted. If there was finally a change to be noted, it was only that you'd sunken deeper down into the muck.

3

The day I decided to leave Hamburg it rained. I'd slept on Little Parrot Street at night. It was located in Altona, down by the harbor. I had no money for the trolley and it was much later in the day before I got out of Hamburg. It was still raining, I was soaked through, but in good spirits; now life was finally going to take on a little shape; now I'd experience the life I'd run away from home to achieve.

A big city's periphery isn't anything especially uplifting; I never felt I could deal with garbage dumps, allotment gardens, storage depots, factory grounds, and cheap tenement houses. Now and then there was a bit of a field, and a tumbledown farmhouse and a lean cow got me to believe that I was in the country now, but right after came an old farmhouse that was fitted up as a hauler's garage, after that came a truck garden and a chemical plant. It was clear that the real farmland still lay far away. In addition, my feet were no longer in shape, there wasn't a dry spot on my body, it was getting to be evening, and I had no idea where to stay the night. I was in no position to begin riding in a car: no driver stops that close to town to pick up a vagabond. I wasn't far from wishing I were back in the seaman's home in Altona.

In the houses along the road the lights were being lit; big trucks with trailers rattled past me on massive tires and splashed me with slush and mud; in front of a dirty sign bespattered by dirt from the road was standing an abandoned circus caravan that looked as though it'd been forgotten; there were still remnants of a poster: *Huge sensation. Direct from New York.* Underneath the picture of a death-rider on a motorcycle there was written in pencil the name of a village and a date. A rusty bicycle frame was standing leaning against one of the caravan wheels. Some place out in the clammy twilight you could hear the sounds from a train being shunted.

But in spite of everything. Now I'd finally experience freedom.

A man rode past me on a bicycle. He was in a raincoat and high boots. On his head he had a uniform cap. He was probably a kind of policeman. When he'd gone a little bit past me, he stopped and got off. It was right under a light—the glint of his buttons and gold braids made me afraid. He began to move over toward me, while he raised one hand and shouted something or other. I didn't have enough presence of mind to scram, or else the dread of the uniform, authority, was in my blood from childhood. My upbringing, you understand. It was impossible for me to imagine that there was an ordinary human being inside the uniform, a human being like all the rest, a human being who on Sundays would lie on a sofa in a boring living room in shirtsleeves and couldn't be distinguished from all other human beings. Here on the highway he was something fear-inspiring, the law, the authorities, and all that stuff. He represented power, society, which caught a vagabond red-handed. When he waved his hand, I had to stop. Stop all at once. It wouldn't even have occurred to me to scram.

Have you ever seen a horse in a fenced-in field where all the grass has been cropped to the root. Outside the fencing there's tall, succulent grass and the fencing isn't that high that the horse wouldn't be able to jump over without a run-up. It stands there looking longingly at that lush, green grass out there, tries by stretching and pointing its muzzle to reach just a little of the splendor, but not for a second does it think of jumping over and satisfying its hunger in the knee-high, fresh lushness. It doesn't occur to it. Not for a second. It doesn't at all suspect that it can be done.

That's the way I stood there on the highway and saw the uniform coming toward me. An order from a uniform quite simply means that it has to be obeyed—not doing it wouldn't even occur to me.

4

I'm sitting here in a people's kitchen like a man who's been knocked out. That might suggest that I have a certain talent for doing the wrong thing, but don't worry, in any event you can rely on my being right when I say it's been my experience that it's a false doctrine that people should speak truthfully. The point is not to speak the truth, but to say what the situation demands—what's most expedient. The times my good upbringing has had the upper hand and lured me into saying the truth, I've almost always gotten into hot water, whereas I've extricated myself from a series of situations with a handy little lie. You have to say the smartest thing there is to say. Sometimes it may be smart to say the truth, but that's rare.

If I'd told the uniform the way things were, I'd have been arrested, expelled from Germany, and sent home to the potted plants and my family's crabby reproaches. That's why I said that I was a German South Jutlander,* a gardener by occupation, who was out looking for work. He remarked that I spoke German badly. I said that my family was Danish, that they spoke Danish at home, but that *I* felt and thought like a German, that my heart was with Germany, and that among other things that was the reason why I'd left home. That seemed to make him sympathetically disposed, and I already thought that I was going to be let off, when it turned out that he'd gained too much sympathy for me to want to let me paddle my own canoe. That wasn't so lucky: I began to be afraid that he was going to invite me home for dinner and it would come out that I'd told him a pack of lies. That's why I said that I'd just eaten, that I'd given up looking for work for today, and asked the way to the train station.

He wanted to go with me part of the way to the station and asked me on the way what he should do with a geranium that wasn't doing well—the leaves were yellow and curled up. I replied that it had to be transplanted right away in fresh earth; maybe he should mix a little sand in the earth and try and put a bit of lime at the bottom of the pot. He was very surprised.

Lime? I confirmed that it'd come to light that a bit of lime could do wonders—it was a relatively new discovery; I'd heard about a gardener in Schleswig who'd specialized in geraniums and the previous year had been on the edge of ruin in that it turned out that all his geraniums, many thousands, were on the verge of dying. The gardener became desperate, his whole existence was on the line; he didn't sleep at night and began to get religious, until one morning, when, careworn, he was wandering around in his hothouses among the dying geraniums, he discovered that a dozen of them that were standing off to the side were thriving splendidly, had fresh green leaves, and were bursting with buds. He took a couple of them inside and knocked them out of the pots to find out what the reason could be. It turned out that there was a little lime lying at the bottom of the pots. He called in the gardener trainee, who'd worked with these plants, and asked him how it happened that there was lime at the bottom of the pots. The gardener trainee became very scared and thought he was going to be fired; he swore that he had no idea how the lime had gotten in there. The gardener pondered about it all night and the next morning he made the drastic decision to transplant all the geraniums and put lime at the bottom. In the course of two weeks all the plants recovered and he was saved from ruin.

Well, I'll be damned, the uniform said. Maybe a guy should try it.

When we reached the station, he suddenly stopped and looked at me thoughtfully, said that he was just going to make a call and that I should wait outside till he was done. Now you stay here, he said. That was an order. And besides, I didn't have any great chance of getting away: he had a bike and I was a stranger in the place. What was it he had to call about? Maybe I should take the chance anyway and try to disappear.

Before I could decide, he came back out. It was right before the departure of a train and he was greeting people left and right. Well, now what do you think, he said, when he came over to me—I've got a job for you. He said it with the donor's suppressed delight, just the way you say: Well, you didn't expect that, did you. Or: I've got a surprise for you—what do you think it might be.

I've got to admit that I wasn't as ecstatic as I should've been. Damn it all, that idiot. If people would really just keep their magnanimity to themselves and let me alone. Now I was right on the verge of being able to realize my dreams of freedom, of the real freedom, and then this stupid ass comes along and spoils the whole thing with his slobbering kindness; if I just hadn't said that I was a German South Jutlander—that was what gave him such sympathy for me; it was right after the vote in South Jutland,* and all the good Germans were convinced that the whole border population loved Germany and was being snatched away from the fatherland and the mother tongue by all imaginable skullduggery. At least the youth. Things were desperate: so now I was going to have let myself be ordered around again. Go and lug around a wheelbarrow. Right on the threshold to freedom. I was lying here with my tail in Hamburg and couldn't get any further. Damn it to hell.

He'd telephoned gardener Guse, a nice man, who'd give me room and board and a small wage for the time being. Then if I were capable, I could become a permanent hand and get a higher wage. I could certainly go down there that very evening. Well, what do you say about that, he repeated and was very proud of having outdone himself. I had an easy time showing that I was overwhelmed, but I had a hard time showing ecstasy. That's certainly wonderful, I said, but don't you think it'd be better if I took the train to Hamburg this evening and returned tomorrow. I mean, I couldn't very well show up at my new job the way I looked. I mean, I wanted to make a good impression at my new job. I mean, I looked like a vagabond, soaked through and filthy, and, I mean, I'd hate for them to think I was.

Bunch of nonsense, said the uniform—really, don't be so sensitive; I'll go along down there and explain the lay of the land.

When we got down to gardener Guse's, the whole family and the staff were sitting in the kitchen eating dinner. It was a big kitchen, spacious, bright, and scoured white. It was cozy and there was a pleasant odor of good food; the crew looked so nice and friendly; when we came in the door, they all turned their newly washed faces toward us; a young girl who was on the way over to the table with a plate of freshly peeled yellow potatoes also stopped and mustered me with a friendly look; she had a pretty face with fresh skin and deep eyes, which looked right at you. That made me a little less spiteful.

5

I don't know whether you can imagine how a hard a time of it I had while I was at gardener Guse's. Those people were as kind-hearted to me as if I'd been their son; my greatest wish was to get away from there and out into freedom on the highway, and the whole world was conspiring against me and preventing me from attaining that freedom. If the Guses had exploited me or treated me like a dog, it would've been easy to get away, but they were so considerate and nice it was infuriating. If Gunhild had just even been ugly, just a little bit ugly, damn it, I could've slipped away. But she was pretty and full of roguishness and sex appeal.* Or if she'd been dismissive, but she was the opposite: after I'd been there two days, I kissed her behind the potting shed and after that day we took walks together in the evening and more than that.

It didn't look as though anything could be done about it. It was impossible to leave the Guses: they gave me clothing, gave me pocket money, never criticized my work, tried to teach me something, gave me German lessons after work, and took me along whenever they were going on trips or to the movies. If I'd come straight from home, it might've helped me that Guse was a socialist—my father the parish deacon considered socialists about the lowest thing on this earth—but the ordinary seamen on the Thurø-schooner had disabused me of those kinds of fallacies.

Besides, I had that business with the policeman's geranium hanging over my head; any day now I expected to see him come into the nursery and call me to account. One day I cautiously asked Guse whether it'd be beneficial to put lime at the bottom of a geranium pot. Guse laughed and said it wouldn't be so beneficial—the geranium would be lucky if it escaped with its life. How the hell could I have come up with that idea. I just replied something to the effect that I'd once heard that it was supposed to be good, but that I'd definitely thought it was a bunch of nonsense.

So however I went about it, I had to try and get away. I hadn't run away from home to go to a nursery and water tomatoes; I'd fled to experience freedom and adventure. If I was lazy and behaved stupidly, Guse'd surely get sore at me—maybe he could even be made so angry that he'd ask me to get lost; in any case, he might well get so peevish that it wouldn't be so hard for me to clear out.

In the meantime, one evening I made the naive slip of confiding in Gunhild. She lay there for a long time without saying anything, which gave me courage to continue and tell her lock, stock, and barrel about my flight from home, that I wasn't a South Jutlander, that I hated work and family life, about my longing to be able to roam about free as a bird without its being anyone's business, and about the policeman's geranium.

Since she still didn't say a word, I felt odd and groped for her head in the dark. When I grazed her cheek, my hand got wet.

I reached up with my arm and turned on the light. Why, you know, the girl was really lying there crying. Maybe it sounds a bit crude, but my first thought, when I saw her beautiful face with her eyes filled with tears lying there on my pillow, was that, of course, girls lying in bed in films cry all wrong: their glycerine tears calmly and tranquilly roll down along each side of their nose, while Gunhild's tears rolled from the outer corner of her eyes and down into each ear. It was a little bit funny.

What are you thinking about? she sniffled. Naturally I couldn't tell her and instead said something about having thought how hard it'd be for me to leave her. With the corners of her nightgown, which was lying at the head of the bed, I dried away her tears and tried to calm her down.

Then she said: I'll go with you.

Fourth Chapter

1

You have to admit that I'd gotten into a difficult situation. How was I to go about making good my escape? How was I going to sneak away like a thief in the night from people who'd treated me that well? I had to do something that could get the Guses, including Gunhild, to despise me profoundly and sincerely. Then I'd be able to leave them with a light heart and live the free life I yearned for so boundlessly.

The following days I was intentionally surly and obstinate, did my work badly, didn't answer when I was spoken to, gave the wrong soil to the plants, insulted one of Guse's best customers, and killed Gunhild's favorite kitten. I noticed their amazement about my changed behavior and began to gloat a little to myself and imagine how Guse would ask me to come into the office, give me an envelope with my wages, speak his mind, and ask me to hurry up and vanish from his house. I'd pretend that I'd gotten fed up with it, and if he then regretted it and said that I was welcome to stay after all, I'd be defiant and say that I'd certainly noticed lately that they didn't care about me and that no power on earth would get me to stay a minute longer.

And before an hour had gone by, I'd be on the highway, free and independent. And in the first bit of woods I came to, I'd go in and fling myself full length underneath a tree, where the Queen Anne's lace grew as tall as a man and where you heard nothing but the insects and the wind. Or maybe on the shore of a lake with yellow and white water lilies, where you could lie and watch the grebes* and see the fish skip along the surface.

One afternoon while I was walking past the potting shed I heard Guse chatting with his wife in there and wound up, actually against my will, hearing what they were talking about.

Guse: Damn it, the lad hasn't been having such an easy time—there's something or other that's tormenting him. If he weren't so withdrawn, we could talk to him and maybe get him on an even keel.

Guse's wife: I mean, he's nothing but a child and naturally he misses the feeling of having a home. He goes around here like a stranger; maybe we should try and look after him a little more and be something for him.

Guse: I like the fellow and feel like trying to talk to him, but it's probably best to leave him alone so he can go work it out for himself. Damn it, at that age people are inclined to go get a bee in their bonnet. It's a pity if he's feeling rotten, but it'll surely pass.

So that was all that I'd gotten out of my fine new tactic. It was enough to drive you to despair. I'd surely never succeed in getting away from there. They'd keep me year after year, and when Guse died some day, I'd inherit the nursery and get married to Gunhild. Good night highway, good night dreams of freedom and all little lakes with white water lilies. Good night adventures and great wide world. Good night extraordinary experiences in small, remote mountain villages.

2

So I decided to talk to Guse. Tell him the lay of the land straight out. One afternoon while we were standing tying up tomatoes in one of the cold greenhouses, he said that I shouldn't tie the bast too tightly around the plants—the staking was just supposed to help hold up the weight of the tomatoes—I shouldn't tie them so the bast cut into the stems. Mr. Guse, I said to him, I feel that I'm not cut out to be a gardener; I'd rather tell you the way it is—I'm no good at it, I'm inadequate, and I'll never get it. I've thought a lot about it and decided to tell you that it's better if I left. If you hadn't been so good to me, I'd have left a long time ago.

Yeah, that was certainly quite a rigmarole, he said and smirked. Nope, my friend, stop taking it so seriously—you're splendidly suited to be a gardener and I'm very satisfied with you. Cheer up and stop taking things so hard.

Yes, but Mr. Guse — — —

No buts about it, he said. Damn it, I think you've got an inferiority complex. Just do your best—I won't demand any more. Nobody can do more than his best, not even Our Lord.

He gave me a push on the shoulder with his fist and looked at me right in the face with his good, keen eyes. Is that all right, he said.

I couldn't deal with it—I tried to avoid his gaze and forgot the attitude I'd finally managed to adopt. He had authority and I'd been brought up to yield to authority. I mumbled something or other and he gave me a pat on the cheek and said:

That's settled.

— My plans with Gunhild also failed. I felt so certain that if the girl loved me, she'd also put that crazy plan about going away with me out of her mind when I explained that I'd feel happier about it. Isn't there perhaps something beautiful about making a sacrifice for the one you love. On the contrary, she became more bent on going along after I'd asked her to stop it.

Altogether I was in a pickle. Now there was only way left—that was to scram from the whole thing one night, leave a note on the table, and ask them to understand why there was nothing else I could do. And thank them for all the good they'd done for me.

3

And then it wound up, after all, going totally differently than I'd imagined. I'd decided to leave the next Saturday. In the evening. I would put a letter on the table up in my room; it wouldn't be found until toward noon the next day. I felt horribly rotten about it, but it had to be done.

On Saturday I was in a strange mood and convinced that all of them could see by looking at me what I had in mind. After knocking off for work I went up to my room and wrote the letter on a piece of Guse's company stationery which I'd taken down in the office.

I still hadn't managed to put the letter in an envelope when

I heard Mrs. Guse calling me. I shoved the letter under the pillow and went down. Would I take a package to the railroad station that absolutely had to go off that very evening. I took the package and hurried off. While I was on the way home, I suddenly saw Gunhild diagonally across the street from me. She looked very agitated. At first I thought she'd found the letter and I wished that I'd never been born. When she caught up with me, she was so short of breath I could barely understand what she was saying. When it finally dawned on me, it chilled my spine: Right after I'd taken the package to the station, Rössler, the policeman, had come and asked for me. When he heard that I wasn't home, he said he'd wait for me. Then he'd gone into the office with Guse and Gunhild had run in my direction to warn me.

Naturally I realized that it wasn't the geraniums—that it was something more serious. Maybe it was just something to do with registering with the police, but of course it might also well be that the police had discovered that I was a foreigner and that I was now going to be arrested and deported. Being greeted by a family deputation at the main train station* with the parish deacon at the head, receiving their forgiveness like a prodigal son, and once again being compulsorily detained in *the fancy sitting rooms*. Go home and see father sitting and writing out birth certificates for sixty øre a piece. And every Sunday morning sit in church and devoutly play hypocrite.

Not on your life. Then it'd be better to be beaten to a pulp as a cabin boy on some ship or other. If there was anyone who'd have me. In any case, I had to get out of Germany. Back then I had very naive notions about the police's methods and thought that the whole machinery would be put on highest alert if I made myself scarce.

Five minutes later I was sitting on the bus to Hamburg and Gunhild was standing back on the road waving and crying. I got a lump in my throat and all of a sudden felt that I was losing so much. Something that maybe was worth more than freedom and adventure. The day before it'd seemed to me that it was crystal clear that my fortune was made if I could just slip away, and now suddenly I could no longer understand why it was actually crystal clear. And there was Gunhild standing on the road looking back at the bus that was driving off and all of a sudden I realized that I loved her, that I couldn't do without her, that she'd been the only thing in my life there was anything good about.

And why then did I absolutely have to leave the people who'd treated me better than any other people. I mean, it wasn't because Rössler had come and asked for me—after all, I would've fled that same evening anyway.

But it was just for a moment. When Gunhild and the nursery's chimney had disappeared from sight, I was on the verge of starting to sing—now I was free, now I was my own master again. No obligations, no bonds—life and freedom would be coming now.

4

There was a full house on Little Parrot Street—I got the last bed that was empty. A Copenhagen beggar-prince who called himself Valby-Povl* was lying in the next bed. The rest of them called him Liar-Povl. He was lying there scratching himself incessantly and talking about scams, while I was lying there thinking about Gunhild and about how I was going to get out of Germany before the police nabbed me. I didn't dare stay more than one night on Parrot Street.

I asked Valby-Povl whether he thought I could slip across the border near Kruså.*

Now listen here, he said, you're a little baby: you don't have an honest piece of paper in your pocket and then you think you can walk across the border. From the German side. I mean, you must have bats in the belfry. You see, a German can run the risk and walk across if he isn't wanted by the police; if the gendarmes take him, he just plays dumb, has no idea that he's right near the border, and so on. A Dane can do that from the Danish side. But a Dane from the German side without papers and wanted by the police, that's the most insane thing I've heard in a long time. Why not get sent home,* approach the consul, and say you've lost your papers. He's a nice man, that consul, he talks to you in a friendly and sympathetic way for half an hour and then says that he's awfully sorry that he can't help you. Just approach him—maybe you can get a ticket to the Salvation Army hostel, where they have almost no lice and where you can get permission to chop wood and sing hymns if you're really well-behaved. Across the border, you say, nooo, damn it, that won't work, pal, but try and talk to the stokers on one of the Danish boats, damn it, they'll help you get home, all right, without asking about your citizenship rights or your religion—just say hello from Valby-Povl, then it'll definitely be okay.

The next day Valby-Povl accompanied me down to the harbor to find a ship for me. After he got me to come clean with my whole story, he felt that I should probably prefer the prescribed way of going home, after all. It could certainly be arranged and it was, well you know, more pleasant.

I tried to let him in on the fact that it was that business with my family. That this way I'd fall right back down into my family's bosom, but under even more difficult circumstances than when I ran away from home. And that it was my plan at some point eventually, maybe not for many years, to return home with a lot of money in my pocket, put up at the Angleterre* and invite the whole family to dine, come on like a big shot, really impress them, and then go off on my way again, out to the great wide world, to new adventures and experiences.

Valby-Povl looked at me disapprovingly. Yeah, you know, I sure thought you were a childish ass. I once knew a guy who took off from home in order to be able to return and show them a guy could turn into somebody without their advice and admonitions. He also wanted to return home on a 2nd class ticket, send a telegram about his arrival, and so on—such a really stupid little pig from a nice home, you understand. He sailed off and saved every penny, didn't smoke, didn't drink, just to be able to go home and annoy his family. Naturally he soon discovered that that isn't the way it's got to be done. So he went ashore and became a dishwasher at a bar in Marseille. That didn't work out either. Then he went to the States, took the hardest drudgery you could get, and discovered once again that it's the hardest work that pays the least. That's a hard and fast rule, old boy, don't ever forget it. The ones who earn the most are the ones who don't do anything; from there the earnings gradually go down and are the lowest for the ones with the longest working hours and the hardest toil. So, after ten years he managed to scrape enough together that he was able to slip back over to Europe, got a job at a box factory in Paris, and tried to be thrifty and industrious. One year after the next went by and he had every possible kind of job, but he never managed to put aside enough to be able to go through with his trip home and invite his family for split pea soup at Bræddehytten.* So he killed a man and took his wallet with 7,000 francs, which was something like a thousand crowns back then, and outfitted himself from head to toe. God, how his family would be annoyed when they saw how dashing he'd become: there they spent their time at home, did their jobs, and were nice and well-behaved; so that's what you got out of going around and being decent and nice—they had to go around with an old overcoat, which was turned inside out, and put margarine on their bread, while a loafer like that could come rolling in from Paris like some kind of man of the world, dashing and elegant, and be patronizing to them and say that they shouldn't lose heart: after all, we can't all come out on top, but, you know, the quiet life has its place too, and so on.

Well, he had to wait about two weeks in Paris before he left, because you could see by looking at his calloused hands how he'd had to slave away, and that of course wasn't part of the plan. He went to the manicure salon every other day, but that didn't help much. In the meantime of course he'd blown some of the money and he began contemplating killing someone else so as not to run the risk of winding up running dry midway. But he couldn't really find the opportunity for it and decided then to go home and pull it off as well as he could, while he still did have some money. He bought a pair of gloves to hide his hands, telegraphed his arrival and travelled third class to Gedser.* In Gedser he bought a ticket second-class and when the train rolled into the main station, he was hanging out of the window of the compartment with a big cigar in his mouth. With a cigar band, you understand.

Sure enough, his family was standing on the platform, but his father was missing. He'd died in the meantime; that was a hitch, because it'd been especially him who was supposed to get annoyed. You see, he was the most respectable one of them all.

Well, the family really didn't wind up being especially impressed; if anything, they were of course happy to see that he was alive and that he hadn't completely gone to the dogs. The man of the world gave his suitcase to a hotel bellboy from one of the big hotels and said that he was very glad to see all of them again, and that he was forced to retire to his room. He was tired from the trip and had a number of business matters to see to, important things, telegrams, and that kind of thing. They felt that he could just as well go home with them and live there; after all, he could presumably manage his business matters, but he said that they were no judge of that—he was forced to live in a proper place to be able to tend to social obligations, but that he'd be very happy if they'd be his guests the following day at Wivel.* For dinner.

The morning of the next day he tried to figure out what such a dinner with wine and extras might well wind up costing and discovered that it corresponded exactly to the amount that he had left. At the dinner he put on a big show, said that these endless trips on the continent with hotel stays tired him a lot, and that he'd begun to consider buying a little bungalow at Lake Fure* to have a place he could withdraw to when he needed a bit of peace and quiet. He let something leak out about his business, about his villa at Lake Garda,* and about the well-known names he was going to meet the following days and discuss business with. He mentioned these famous persons as equals; some of them he called by their first names and recounted incidents from their private lives.

He'd asked the doorman at the hotel to call Wivel at half-past twelve and to inform him whether any telegrams from abroad had arrived. At half-past twelve a servant came through the room and asked loudly for President Andersen from Paris. He got up with an exhausted expression, apologized to his family—you certainly never got any peace and quiet—and went to the phone.

When he returned, he informed his family that a telegram had come and unfortunately he had to travel to Berlin the next morning. He hugged all of them and promised to think of each one in his will.

Next morning he had thirty-five øre left. He'd given his last five-crown coin to his sister's little boy to buy candy with. Then he took the trolley out to the last stop in Valby and walked out to the highway. It's not that easy to be on the tramp when you've got fancy clothes on, but after he'd been lying in haystacks and barns for a couple of nights, he began to look like a human being. He tramped through all of Germany and one fine day reached Paris, where he joined the Foreign Legion. After he'd been there for two years, he managed to run away, and now he's bumming in Hoboken.

5

Two days later I was standing on the wharf in Esbjerg.* The stokers on a Danish boat had stowed me away without demanding anything in return other than my keeping my mouth shut. I had a couple of German thousand mark bills on me, but they weren't worth anything—no one wanted to exchange them.* Outside the seaman's home I got to talking with a coal trimmer,* who advised me to go out and hustle up a crown and spend the night at the travelling journeyman's hostel. I looked in on some villas on the outskirts of town, which were nicely situated and looked nice, but I quickly learned that if I asked for a couple of øre for a night's lodging, they shut the doors again just like that. Without a word. I became piqued and tried it next door. Same result. I certainly wish people would answer you when you ask them something—it certainly doesn't cost anything. I was just on the verge of giving up, but I was hungry and thought that in any case they probably wouldn't deny me a couple of sandwiches. I rang the bell at a small red-brick house with hollyhocks, the kind of house where the woman of the house herself is in the kitchen, and asked for a little bite to eat. The woman said that she was in a hurry, but asked if she mightn't give me ten øre. By now the thought of food had made me tremendously hungry, and I traipsed through the whole strip of villas asking for food. Everywhere I got money, but no food. That's the way people are—the only need they respect is the stomach's. And once you've convinced them of your need, they just try to get out of it as easily as possible. In reality people are insensitive to a fellow human being's difficulties; when they give you something, it's only a result of a kind of morality in them, not at all because they feel something while doing it. It's something that custom requires if you want to be a respected citizen and enjoy others' and your own respect.

Besides, people like being introduced to distress when they themselves are living off the fat of the land and having a good time of it. It produces such a pleasant sensation. The only thing they demand is that the distress that's being introduced isn't too boring, too common. And naturally it has to be distress that packs a wallop. The best thing is if the distress is indescribable and linked to an uncommonly dreary fate. In part it has the advantage that people can then feel moved—something they of course ordinarily have to pay through the nose for; if a play or a film can get them to cry, that's regarded as as fine as it gets, but at the same time such a fate, if it's a bit peculiar, has the advantage that you can tell about it the next time there's an evening party. It's a very refined and indirect method of informing people that you have a heart for the poor creatures who come to your door begging. You don't have to say that you gave the beggar something—that's so coarse; being familiar with the poor creature's story shows that you've been looking after him and to such a degree that you've gained his confidence to boot.

Naturally the vagabond can't tell the same story everywhere. It has to be adapted to the circumstances and the people he's telling it to. The point here is to develop a certain psychological sense. To a clergyman you can often successfully say that you've been in prison; he's shaken by the fact that for a change he's dealing with an out-and-out sinner, and of course Our Lord's happier about the converted sinner than about those who've always been well-behaved. To a doctor you can safely say that a quack ruined your father and contributed to his dying prematurely; with an employer you can say that the labor union bureaucracy knocked you out. With a wholesale merchant* you have to be a jaunty fellow, a real man, who's tried a little of everything.

Back then, of course, I was, if anything, a complete beginner, but people themselves very quickly educate a vagabond of normal intelligence to tell a story. Otherwise he simply won't get anything. Since I was, of course, very young and raised to be modest, I never elbowed my way ahead and that way I mainly got women as my clientele. Women prefer a story that's touching. Since I was a bit near-sighted and people noticed that now and then and I'd be asked whether it had caused me difficulties, in a way it happened completely automatically that I'd explain that I'd gone out to sea when I was fourteen years old and almost served my apprenticeship when my eyes began to cause difficulties; it'd gotten worse and worse, and by now I was no longer capable of doing the work that was required. I'd had to stop sailing and was now without an occupation. In the meantime my mother had died; my father had died when I was little. I had the hope some day of eventually becoming a brush-maker. A doctor who'd examined my eyes hadn't wanted to hide from me that possibly I'd lose my vision completely. How long it would take he couldn't say. Life was hard, but of course you had to learn to accept the vicissitudes of fortune with good cheer; you had to be brave. The story had sprung up on its own; it was actually, if anything, the women themselves who made it up with their questions. For example, the little filler about the doctor, who didn't exist in the first versions of the story: A friendly woman had offered me coffee in her kitchen and pumped me in the meantime for my story. When I got to that business with the near-sightedness and underscored it by constantly fumbling for the cup, she asked me whether my eyes in fact were still getting worse, to which I answered yes. Then all of a sudden she got a craving for a sensation and asked me in an agitated voice whether I thought that I'd eventually lose my sight totally, become blind. I looked mournful and confirmed it with a weak yes. After that she turned aggressive and asked why I actually felt that way. I searched my brain for a suitable answer and then said that a doctor had said it. That was like grist for her mill; she was deeply moved and wanted to know whether the doctor had said how long it would take before I became blind. I replied that the doctor couldn't say with certainty. That satisfied her immensely—I got an extra cup of coffee and fifty øre.

6

I went begging in Esbjerg for about a week. I hadn't the slightest urge to realize my dreams of the free and easy life on the road here in Denmark, where I lived; it was going to be in a foreign country, in other surroundings, and would have to be shelved for the time being. Maybe I'd try to get to France. In France there are mountains and rivers, vineyards along the highways, where you can stuff yourself like a pig with all the grapes you'd care to; in the monasteries they give you a night's lodging and breakfast free and wish you luck on your journey if you're going on. Besides, Frenchmen are said to be immoral—France would surely be an excellent country to be on the tramp in.

But for the time being I had to deal with the problems that were more immediate and hope that a way of getting to France would turn up. I'd gotten to know a man named Schmidt. Schmidt was no ordinary vagabond: he travelled with a suitcase and didn't leave one town till he had enough money to be able to go by train to the next. When things didn't go so splendidly and he had to live in a travelling journeyman's hostel, his suitcase would be at the left-luggage office at the train station. In the suitcase he had clean underwear and a couple of extra pairs of pants, a jacket for indoors, and a toothbrush. He intimated that he knew a thing or two and that he preferred begging for paper money than for small change. If there absolutely had to be begging at all. He called it swindling and felt that it raised him above the rest of the residents of the travelling journeymen's hostel and emphasized that his method had to be regarded as labor-saving, more lucrative, and lying on a higher social plane. Incidentally, he claimed to be the king's illegitimate son and to have taken out a patent on a revolutionary invention that would make him a millionaire when the formalities had been taken care of and the manufacturing could be started on. He could sell the patent tomorrow for a dizzying sum, but intended to exploit his invention himself and not to let some damned sharks run off with most of the profit. He had time to wait till matters were arranged; a few days ago he'd contemptuously rejected a flattering offer from Sir Basil Zaharoff, the armaments prince.* In addition he composed little verses about butterflies and girls' breasts, but, in spite of countless requests, he didn't want to publish them since he regarded it as in bad taste to expose his spiritual life to the masses.

I was very impressed with Schmidt, and when he claimed that Esbjerg was a dung-hole and suggested that we travel together to Odense,* I felt very flattered and was only afraid that he'd regret it before we got going. He was very interested in what experiences I'd had and I laid it on a bit thick, since otherwise I didn't feel that it would interest a man of such considerable stature. For example, I told him that the Thurø-schooner had been stranded on the Scottish coast and that the rescue work had been very arduous and perilous; I'd been the last to be rescued because I absolutely insisted that the skipper go into the breeches buoy* before me, since he had a wife and children in Svendborg* and at any moment the ship could be smashed in the raging breakers. I was very modest and wouldn't accept the praise for heroism Schmidt made me the object of, and said that I was, of course, only doing my duty.

So we had to get the money for the train tickets to Odense, and Schmidt said that that'd be a piece of cake if I'd just do as he said. We went to the post office and here Schmidt wrote a letter that was supposed to look as if it'd been written by my mother in Copenhagen. The letter was a request to me to come home immediately because she'd gotten me a job at a soap factory. Unfortunately she couldn't send me money for the trip, since she didn't have any, but she hoped that I'd be able to manage that matter myself, since the condition for my being able to get the job was that I start work right away. In a P.S. there were greetings from my little sister and the news that uncle Hans had gotten an intestinal infection and had to be operated on.

Schmidt crumpled the letter a bit and left a couple of fingermarks on it so it would look natural, after which Schmidt stuck the letter in my pocket. We walked together along the street while Schmidt explained my task to me. A dentist lived in a villa at the edge of town: I was supposed to approach him, explain to him that I'd gotten into a difficult situation, that I'd heard he was a man who secretly tried to do good, and show him the letter from my mother. Then the nice dentist would give me money for the trip to Copenhagen, and we could go to Odense that very evening.

Schmidt was waiting on the corner while I walked up toward the villa. I felt rotten and, if anything, like running away from the whole business, but I felt Schmidt's eyes on the back of my head and continued automatically in through the villa's garden gate and up to the house. When I rang the bell, my hands were clammy with cold sweat. A maid answered the door. I introduced myself and asked whether I might be permitted to speak to the dentist; I was led into a waiting room and was asked to wait for a moment. I sat down on a wicker chair and began leafing through an old weekly, but the letters danced before my eyes, and I began considering the possibility of disappearing through the window.

Just then the dentist came. I got up and my cheeks got hot. He was an elderly man with a friendly manner. I suppose I talked very inarticulately, but still I did manage to explain what had brought me to him. He didn't seem to take me seriously; he had such a facetious, ironic way about him. I wanted to make a good impression and informed him that my father had been a parish deacon before he died five years earlier. Well, the dentist said, that doesn't mean you still couldn't be a decent person. I let him read the letter; he stood for a long time pondering it and then said that he really believed that for a change it was an honest person who'd looked him up. Then he took out his wallet, gave me twenty crowns, and asked whether I was very fond of my uncle. I nearly died of agitation and emotion and suddenly began crying. Against my will. Come, come, he comforted me, now don't take it so seriously—I mean, it's not major surgery.

That was the first time in my life I had so much money, and after I'd said goodbye to the dentist and walked out through the garden, I felt that it was senseless for me to have to share with Schmidt; it was quite ample if he got five crowns for having written the letter—it was no mean fee—I was the one who'd had the work and the trouble, and the ten crowns were sufficient for us to get to Odense. If he felt that we didn't have enough as it was, I mean he could approach another dentist—I'd be really glad to write a letter he could take along.

Since I imagined that I was being observed by Schmidt from some place or other, I had to be cautious and separate the two ten-crown bills down in my pocket and in a natural way manage to transfer one bill over into another pocket. When I got the chance, I could put it in a safer place.

Schmidt was waiting for me around the corner. I intimated to him that it was a difficult task and requested that the next time he gave me the address for a scam, he also give me one where it wasn't practically impossible to get money. Nevertheless, I'd succeeded in hitting the dentist up for ten crowns; we needn't have bothered with the letter—he hadn't wanted to look at it at all, he'd said that I was a damned swindler, and the fact that I was able to get money at all was due to my having put on a mask and saying I wouldn't leave the villa till I'd gotten some money. So as far as I was concerned, the dentist could call the police as much as he damn pleased. Then he'd mumbled something and forked over a ten'er.

Schmidt looked very doubtful about my explanation, but he accepted it all the same and even praised me because I'd been so tough.

7

That same evening we got to Odense and the following days were spent on scams that Schmidt arranged and I carried out. I put aside everything that I could justify and hid the bills in the sweatband of my hat. Those were amusing and exciting days back then in Odense. We went for walks in Fruens Bøge* and Munkemose.* Schmidt composed nice verses and thought up new inventions, while I looked at the black swans and dreamed about the real freedom as a vagabond in southern Europe.

We were living in a little hotel down by the train station where the proprietor was very suspicious and already after four days presented us with a bill that we had no money to pay, that is, apart from the bank notes that were lying in the sweatband of my hat and that I was, of course, quite simply prevented from disclosing that I had. The proprietor looked very threatening and since we feared the police more than anything else on this earth, we had to try and figure out a way to calm him down.

Schmidt took care of that. In the afternoon we went down to a little cafe where some girls hung out who lived by street-walking. We fell in with a beautiful, black-haired girl, who was called Odense's nightingale, and she promised to help us manage the proprietor. That happened in the following way:

The nightingale called up the hotel and said: Call from Copenhagen. Go ahead, please. Then she gave the receiver to Schmidt, who put a handkerchief over the mouthpiece and waited a bit, after which, in a distant voice, he asked for deputy director Schmidt. When it turned out that the deputy director wasn't in, Schmidt asked the proprietor to tell Mr. Schmidt that there was a general delivery letter for him, that a money order would follow, and that factory owner Thrige* requested a personal conversation with the deputy director.

When we got home in the evening, the proprietor was unusually amiable, and it wasn't until a week had gone by that in all modesty he was so bold as to put a bill on our writing table.

The following night a sensational burglary took place in the center of Odense. The window in a big jewelry store had been smashed and objects worth thousands of crowns were removed. When we read about it in the newspaper in the morning, Schmidt's face turned green with alarm: we have to get out of town, he said, the police are going to be combing all the hotels and arresting everybody who can't explain what they're up to in Odense. And even if we can probably prove that it's not us, we'll get into a bunch of trouble anyway, we'll be sent to serve a prison sentence for nonpayment of child support for an illegitimate child,* and so on—so, let's get out of town and right away.

In fact, on second thought it turned out to be more difficult to get out of town than to stay in it. We didn't dare go to the train station—naturally the police were there. The same was true of the bus stations. So we had to leave town on foot and avoid the main road till we'd gotten a good ways outside of Odense; there we could stop the bus to Middelfart* and go on.

We did, we walked along the villa roads and byways till we'd got two miles outside of town. There we met up with the main road and hid in a little grove that bordered on the road, and we started waiting for the bus. That took almost three hours. When it came, we went and stood out on the roadway and waved. There was plenty of room in the vehicle: apart from us there was only a fat travelling salesman in a well-ironed suit with a pale yellow leather briefcase and an old woman with a basket.

A little further on the woman got off, and the driver sold us tickets and informed us that the bus wasn't going to Middelfart, but only to Enslev.* And that there wasn't a bus going to Middelfart that day.

So we had to spend the night in Enslev. I thought that was amusing, but Schmidt, who was a city person, got crabby and sat the rest of the way bellyaching about the bad luck that had pursued him since the day he was born.

8

We rented ourselves a room at the inn and to while away the time, till it was time to go to bed, we sauntered around the village and its environs. Schmidt was in possession of a clothes brush that could fit in an inside pocket—once in a while he took it out and brushed the cuffs of his trousers. He was very meticulous about his appearance, incessantly using a comb and nail cleaner, straightening his tie, and pulling up his jacket at the neck. I liked talking to him most of all when we were alone; as soon as there were other people nearby, everything he said and did was meant only for them.

We sat down under a willow tree, one of these pollarded* willows, you know, and watched the sunset. Schmidt had spread his handkerchief out on the grass and sat cautiously to spare his suit. He used to say that his appearance was his weapon in the struggle for his daily bread, his tool, and that every decent craftsman maintains his tool in fine condition.

The sun was a big, red ball that was descending behind a little grove; I thought it was so nice—I wonder whether there's anything in this world more peaceful than a village on Funen at sunset. There was a ladybug sitting on my hand and I let it fly up to Our Lord and ask for good weather tomorrow, because, I mean, you just do it—you learned it as a child*—and at the same moment that you see that beautiful little insect, it's as if you've gotten a cue and you just have to get going with the ceremony. As if a button were being pushed. If you see a shooting star, you hurry up and make a wish for something or other—you've learned to do that and you don't dare not do it. Sometimes I've felt like trying never to do what I'd learned I should do, but always the exact opposite. Yeah, like trying outright to do everything that's forbidden. Literally buying a copy of the penal code and trying all the crimes in alphabetical order. Not in order to do harm to anyone, but to get a little sense of freedom; it was more the desire to do something really wild, something in the way of getting up on a roof in a nightshirt and playing a harp.

It was when I'd let the ladybug fly to Our Lord that Schmidt let me in on his extraction, his noble ancestry. He looked stiffly and asked whether I'd actually never thought about whom he resembled. I hadn't, but tried to figure it out in a hurry to cover up my stupidity. He asked me to really look at him. I looked at him penetratingly, but couldn't think of who it was. Then try and look at my profile, he said and turned to the side. Since I still just sat there staring without being able to figure it out, he became a bit irritated and asked whether I still couldn't see it. Ashamed, I had to admit that I hadn't discovered it yet.

For a long time he sat silently, looking ahead and mumbling that maybe it was really best that way. I was sorry about having hurt him and said that I'd very much like to know who it was he looked like. Since he was still sitting there looking as if he were absorbed in somber reflections, I became earnest and said that he should tell me. He appeared to be appeased and asked whether I'd never seen a Danish stamp before. I admitted I had, but didn't grasp what he meant. Silently he took an envelope out of his pocket and handed it to me. I took it and looked at the stamp. It was a ten-øre stamp. I sat for a long time looking at it—it looked very uninteresting. There was a head on it of a handsome, fairly young man with a nice part, the king. Suddenly it struck me: The King.* It was the king he resembled. God did he resemble the king—only the king was better-looking. On the stamp at least.

Schmidt looked at me triumphantly: Yeah, that's the way it is. He nodded gloomily ahead and said: And here I am sitting by the roadside, a prince by blood, who has to beg for my food from ignorant farmers, a scion of the House of Oldenburg* who has to tramp around and degrade himself to keep alive.

9

The next morning we got up early and went down to the dining room to get morning coffee; we'd decided to walk to Middelfart. We'd slept well in spite of the clammy, starched sheets and the heavy down quilts. It was a lovely morning, the sun flooded into the dining room, which was neat and clean, and the coffee was wonderful.

While we were drinking it, we couldn't avoid noticing that the innkeepers were watching us in a strangely suspicious way. Schmidt whispered to me that it was that damned jewelry robbery, and that the stupid innkeeper, damn it, had probably called the police and said they could pick up the jewel thieves here.

We hurried up and paid and left. When we'd gone a little bit down the road, we turned and saw that both innkeepers were standing in the doorway following us with their eyes.

At the first byroad we turned off, but we hadn't been walking more than ten minutes when we were overtaken by a car that stopped crosswise on the road in front of us. Four men poured out of the car and pounced on us, handcuffed us, and hauled us into the vehicle. When we were sitting there, one of them asked triumphantly where we were intending to go. When we said we were going to Middelfart, he said that they were too and we could ride with them. It was the police.

Fifth Chapter

1

We sat in detention for two days in Middelfart. The reason for our arrest was that we'd called attention to ourselves by virtue of our peculiar flight from Odense. Which, of course, we'd undertaken precisely to avoid arrest.

Now when I sit here today and have to talk about that time, I can't help noticing that I took everything so damn seriously back then. It was the first time I'd been arrested and I was so shaken up, as if I were going to go to the electric chair; I cried at night in my cell and when I finally fell asleep, I dreamed about my mother. I couldn't eat anything, and during the interrogations I shook all over and they had to drag every word out of me. Of course, I've been arrested so many times since, and today it doesn't bother me any more than someone asking me for a match. There's nothing remotely dramatic about being arrested—everything becomes habit. Young offenders and newly hatched detectives still enjoy the situation and try to soak it for as much romanticism as possible, but afterward it's very straightforward—just come along now up to police headquarters, he says—and then you slouch along and on the way you chat about anything but; after a while arrests become so uninteresting that you try to avoid them just because they're boring and devoid of excitement.

And it's just the same for most of the experiences surrounding a vagabond's life as for the arrests. The first time an experience makes a deep impression on you, but the repetitions are tiring and life as a tramp gets just as monotonous and kind of boring as work in a factory or an office—everything becomes habit.

That's probably why I talked at such length about the first period of time I was out in life; what I experienced in that period stands sharp and distinct in my memory; later the experiences made less of an impression on me, and there's a long period of time that I've completely forgotten—it's not possible for me to recall what I was doing during that time and in what country I was living.

What I can say about the following years is that I never succeeded in becoming a real vagabond: every time I was about to realize my dreams of the real freedom, something or other got in the way—I got a job or got arrested or got sick or whatever might get in the way. Maybe it was because, when push came to shove, I didn't dare. I mean, I was brought up to be a slave, to do whatever I was told, and, to be perfectly blunt, I myself wasn't capable of taking responsibility for my own life.

2

Well, as far as Middelfart's concerned, we were in fact released after two days; they probably could've found something or other to get us in trouble over, but if we weren't the jewel thieves, they just wished to get rid of us as quickly as possible. An officer accompanied us to the ferry* and made sure that we were really leaving their nice little town. Schmidt claimed that his noble ancestry was the cause of our sudden release—an exchange of telegrams with a high-ranking person in Copenhagen had done the trick.

We parted company in a Jutland town where a pastor had taken an interest in me and managed to place me as a hotel porter at the town's temperance hotel—the circumstances had developed such that I was forced to take a job. It was while I was at the temperance hotel that I got the glasses—I'd used my nearsightedness as an excuse for mistakes so often that one day the hotel's owner lost her patience and ordered me to the doctor to get glasses.

I think that the glasses have had a big influence on my fate—I wound up looking more intelligent and more pious. That was very fortunate for me in many situations, but it made me have a hard time making contact with women. That's why on my days off I used to leave them at home, but then on the other hand I had to put up with contemptuous looks from my female acquaintances when they saw me at the train station, where I was forced to wear the glasses to see the passengers.

3

My pious, bespectacled face secured me a promotion: Every other week I had to act as night clerk. That was a nice cushy job: I'd sit comfortably in a wicker chair with a little green lamp above my head and read a novel every night. My only work consisted in letting the guests in, eating a huge plate of open-face sandwiches, and shining shoes in the morning. I slept during the morning, got up and ate lunch, and spent the afternoons taking walks. It was a glorious existence.

Unfortunately I misused it. And lost it. Along with the open-face sandwiches went half a pale, light beer,* but I could get a real pilsner fit for a human being* instead, if I paid the difference. Since I loved sitting at night fancying that I was a big deal, I bought half a bottle of schnapps and kept it in my closet. When it was three o'clock in the morning, I'd spread out a big napkin on the desk, set out the open-face sandwiches, arrange the plate, knife and fork, beer glass and schnapps glass, and get myself settled. I'd clear my throat and try to look dignified while I inspected the open-faced sandwich. Then I'd pour a beer and schnapps and take pains to believe that I'd never done anything else but have breakfast with beer and schnapps. In the parish deacon's home a breakfast like that was totally unheard of and, as far as I know, had taken place only the two times the pastor had been on a visit. I'd draw out the meal as long as possible, and between each sandwich I'd lean back in the wicker chair and read the newspaper. To be sure, it was old at that point, but in one way or another that was part and parcel of the image of a breakfast. When I was finally done, I'd wipe my mouth with my napkin, pour myself a cup of coffee, and light a cigar. Before that time I actually didn't care for cigars—I'd smoked only cigarettes—but I realized that the cigar was an important part of the ceremony.

Afterwards I'd set about dreaming about the extraordinary and sensational things that some day I'd eventually perform. That keyed me up immensely, stimulated me, and caused me to be in a position to treat a guest in a friendly and courteous way, even if he was rude and insolent. It was a lovely time.

Gradually I wouldn't be content with one schnapps, but would drink a couple with coffee. I wasn't used to alcohol and the light intoxication better enabled me to dream. After a while, this night-time breakfast became a necessity for me, and all afternoon and evening I looked forward to it downright devotedly.

But it cost money and I wasn't earning much. That's why I began to avail myself of the many little illegal possibilities there were to earn a little extra, and for a long time things went well, so well that I always had money and in the afternoon, when I was off, I could go into one of the little taverns, drink a beer, and play billiards. After a while these afternoons also became necessary for me and I became bolder and bolder in my little transactions to procure money.

It was beginning to be rumored in town that the new night clerk wasn't that difficult to deal with for people who wished to rent a double room but didn't look especially married, and that he didn't pay attention if they left the room again after a couple of hours, just as he didn't always take it that seriously whether their names were entered in the guest book. One day, while I was standing on the platform waiting for passengers, a doctor, the one who'd prescribed glasses for me, got out of the train in a largish party. When he saw me, he said in a loud voice to the others: Well, there we have the temperance hotel night clerk—God gives his mercy to the lovers. There was general tittering and it was difficult for me to pretend that I hadn't heard the comment.

About a week later I was called in by the hotel owner; she was from Vendsyssel* and in the Inner Mission.* She asked me how it could happen that No. 12 had been used that night without its being apparent from the guest register. I dealt with it by saying it was an oversight, and since I hadn't settled up the accounts for the night yet, I got away with a reprimand.

Things went well for a while—I'd become more cautious and thought that it'd be all right and that the previous night clerks had doubtless used the same practices; but one evening she came home from a parish council* meeting and was blue in the face from being so worked up. She didn't explain anything at all, but shouted nonstop that I should leave, that I should vanish from her house and do so right away. That night I had to live in a hotel myself. I rented a cheap room at The Harmony.

4

That was the year there was an exhibition in Gothenburg.* I went to the police and got a passport. The constable joked and didn't make a secret of the fact that he knew the reason for my trip. The whole town appeared to know—the hotel proprietor was obviously the last to find out.

I traveled to Gothenburg on the steamer. On board there were two unemployed printers who were going to tour Sweden; back then it didn't matter where you went in Europe—you'd meet Danish printers on the trip. They had a fine benefits system, travelled by train from town to town, and travelled around like other tourists.* I wanted to feel in the same class with such widely travelled and experienced persons and I lied rather flagrantly about where I'd been and what I'd experienced. In the beginning they were very impressed and I let myself be encouraged by my success to give my fantasy free rein. Finally it got too crude for them; they told me to shut up and went down to the restaurant to drink coffee.

When we got to Gothenburg, I rented a room at a hotel on Post Street and went out to look at the town. I had about 50 crowns and decided to feel like a tourist. The next day I went to the exhibition and looked at the things that were exhibited as if I were a good judge of them. That's an obligation you have when you go to an exhibition and everyone around you is doing the same. In addition, you walk around studying things scrupulously that don't interest you in the slightest and that you've seen displayed hundreds of times in shops without having bothered to cast a glance at them.

I was an exhibition visitor with sun glasses and my hands full of brochures until my money ran out. I was just barely able to pay my hotel bill and buy a train ticket to Borås.* In the train I met a travelling magician. His name was Bror Wallen and he wanted to use me as an assistant in return for paying for my lodgings wherever we appeared. I'd have to find the money for food in some mysterious way or other—he wasn't going to get involved in that, as long as I didn't compromise his racket.

It went well for about a week: we visited the restaurants, got the proprietor's permission to perform, and when he'd displayed his tricks with me as assistant, I went around with a plate and collected. Bror Wallen's eyes followed the plate incessantly—it was impossible for me to get any cash out of it for myself.

I had to beg for food and money for cigarettes in the villas on the outskirts of the city. I'd hoped to be able to learn something from the magician, but he knew very little; he was an unemployed carpenter from Gothenburg and it was but a month since he'd bought "The Little Magician"* and taught himself some of the most common tricks. People took it very good-naturedly, but of course it didn't produce big money.

I said goodbye to Bror Wallen, gave my suitcase as security at a hotel to have a place to keep my clothes, and took to the road.

5

Now I was once again finally standing face to face with the existence I'd dreamed so much about, the life, the free, unfettered life on the road. I tried to put into practice the little fantasy images I'd been lavishing so much care on; I lay down by the side of the road and said to myself that I was free now. But after two minutes had elapsed, I got up again and walked on. Somehow or other I was restless; it was as if I didn't dare lounge away a totally ordinary workday, as if I had a kind of bad conscience.

I had the feeling of doing something illegal, and every time I found myself a nice spot to lounge in and some people came walking by, this idiotic dread came over me that they'd interfere with my business and order me off into some unfree existence or other.

I figured that this feeling would gradually pass, but by the time four days had gone by, I'd taken a job on a farm where they needed people to help with the hay harvest.

And just as things went on that occasion, that's the way things always went during the following years: I was constantly working toward being free, and when push came to shove, I didn't dare give in to my desire for freedom—it was the upbringing I'd received that incessantly ruined it for me.

There's no reason to deal with these years in more detail. I experienced a lot, had hundreds of odd jobs, was always on the move from one place to another—I was in Germany, Norway, Holland, France. Once in a while I came home to Denmark; as a rule, that was when the consulate in some country or other had sent me home, and it took only a few days before I left the country again. When I needed to, I managed with petty crimes, sat in jail a couple of times, I was sick a couple of times; in Marseille I was laid up in the hospital for six months—it didn't quite correspond to what people understand by a hospital here in this country.

I think these stays in hospitals and jails have had a certain influence on me: I got time to read a lot, devoured lots of novels and works of popular science—at the Welfare Office shelter in Berlin they called me the professor. But my glasses probably did their part too; besides, I think the nickname obligated me to be smarter than the rest of them; nicknames obligate you to do what people expect you to do.

6

That turned into an obsession with me—that stuff about freedom. In the first years, it had been, if anything, an unconscious urge: as a child I was never allowed to do anything, everything was forbidden, and I'm certain that that's why I later had such a desire to do everything that was forbidden.

Now you mustn't think I go in for philosophizing—I don't want you to think that I fancy I'm smarter than other people—but you have to admit that as you see me sitting here, almost thirty-five years old, with tattered clothes, scruffy, with a shattered eyeglass lens, at a people's kitchen with a cup of coffee in front of me I got by begging, a down-and-out person who doesn't even have the brutality that's required to be down and out, it might damn well look as if my life had been smashed to bits.

And it would be easy to say that I myself had ruined my chances by being a twirp, a guy without a backbone and with criminal tendencies. And maybe in a way that's true enough, but why did I turn into a twirp, why wasn't I able to become a rough customer like the others or stay in the box I'd been put in. After all, I'm a grown man now and have to confess that I was lying out there in my rusted crate of a car crying because I felt my life was wasted, because I wasn't able to have a job like other people and go home after work to a woman and a couple of children, who were waiting for you and said *dad*. And, I mean, a person has just one life and it can't be lived all over again.

It's possible it was cowardly of me not to want to take the responsibility myself, but I'm certain that it was my nice upbringing that's to blame for my fate. Of course, I'm also not the only one like that: all around I've met countless guys of the same caliber as me, guys from nice homes with a nice upbringing and all that kind of thing, and when we took the trouble to chat about it, we've always agreed that we were the ones on the right side, we were the only normal ones. That the other people were the ones who, to be blunt, didn't have enough guts to resist the upbringing—that it obliterated them.

I understand really well if this stuff doesn't interest you: You've given me a helping hand and in return wanted to hear my story, my experiences, the stuff I've pulled. Naturally, you don't care about this nonsense I'm sitting here dishing up, but there's something here, you understand, that little by little has become so important to me by now that I can't get on with life, so to speak, until I succeed in understanding it. When people say to children: *You're not allowed to*, they instantly answer: *Why not*. But little by little, as they grow up and either don't get any answer or find out that that's the way it is because that's the way it's supposed to be, they don't ask any more and you can palm off on them any prohibition that's necessary—they don't even ponder any more about *why*, but are content with taking note of it; to be perfectly blunt, they've been subdued, and the employer and the state can do whatever they want with them—they've learned to obey. And to obey without asking *why*.

And in a way that's become their good fortune—they've been assigned a box to be in, they get their tuft of hay at the prescribed times, and if they get a stomach ache, someone fetches the veterinarian for them. And the real living human being in their heart of hearts breathes in innocent little affairs, when they're not under observation; in small dark streets they violate the sixth commandment, and if they can't get away with violating the rest of them any other way, then they do it in their dreams. And that's the way life goes for them—their real self secretly lives side by side with the official one and they constantly have to keep a sharp lookout so that the former doesn't compromise the latter.

But if the upbringing is too total and completely walls up the real self so it can't breathe, it either has to be smothered or break its way out. And maybe that's the way things stand with me.

7

But naturally I wasn't thinking about all that back then. I was just trying to find some way or other of living, which I could feel right about, and little by little, as I suffered defeats, I became less scrupulous about morality, or rather, little by little, I got a different morality.

It was while I was a globetrotter in the South of France that

I discovered that I was a success when I was immoral and a failure when I behaved nicely. If I told a whopping lie, I achieved what I wanted to, if I stuck to the truth, things went wrong. Another thing was that I always got afraid when I was a success that way and didn't dare hold on to the advantages I'd obtained. That way life incessantly forced me to act immorally and afterwards let my good conscience appear on the scene and destroy the fruits of my immorality. I became a globetrotter because I couldn't come up with anything better. I'd gone to Nice, where I felt there'd be lots of opportunities for a plucky man. I lived in a small hotel on the rue Marceau and while I went around waiting for an opportunity to turn up, the bill got bigger and bigger. The only food I got in those days was the coffee I had brought up to the room. Every morning I got coffee with warm milk and bread and butter; they called it petit dejeuner and there wasn't a crumb left when I got up in the hopes of finding a cigarette stub; I knew very well there weren't any, but I looked anyway. In the afternoon I went back to my room and rang for the maid to bring me up a cup of coffee, but after a few days I was so sick with hunger that I also went back in the evening and ordered coffee. Of course, that was a stupid thing to do—I mean that way they were bound to discover I was out of money—but I simply couldn't help it. I'd tried many ways to shore up my reputation in order to extend my credit—I'd written postcards to myself with flattering invitations and all that kind of stuff—but when I also began to come back in the evening to get coffee, they saw through me and the next morning I got the bill. I got a three-day grace period which I used to smuggle out of the hotel the things I needed most. I had a big backpack I'd once bought in Lyon from a Danish journeyman carpenter who lacked money for food; I filled it with the most important of my possessions and slipped out of the hotel safe and sound, went across to the train station and deposited them in the left-luggage office; when I left the hotel again later in the day, my pockets were stuffed with other things; I went back across to the station, asked to borrow my backpack for a minute and emptied out my pockets into it. I continued like that the next two days and that way left behind at the hotel only a worthless suitcase devoid of anything of value. In the meantime I paid a visit to the Danish consul and managed to persuade him to give me a ticket to Marseille, which, with a little ingenuity and a fictitious telephone call, I managed to get refunded at the travel agency. Afterward I had my picture taken and went to a printer and got him to make some picture postcards with my picture and a text, which recounted that I was on a round-the-world tour, stated which countries I'd passed through, and indicated the future route. Underneath, in bold type, there was a request to people to support my interesting project by buying a card. The cards cost more than I had money for, but the printer let himself be talked into delivering half of the cards for the money I had—then later I was to pick up the rest.

After the three days at the hotel had passed, the cards still weren't ready and so I asked for an extension of an extra couple of days, by reference to the possibility that money might be coming to me from Denmark any day now. I was allowed to live there for two more days, but then I was kicked out. They kept my suitcase as security. I had to spend that night on the Promenade des Anglais.* The next morning the cards were ready and I made use of them right away; I went into a cafe right across from the printer's and asked the proprietor for permission to sell the cards to his patrons. I got permission by a hand gesture and afterward I went around and put a card in front of every patron. After having waited a bit, I went over to the table I'd put the card on first and took up my position and waited. I was lucky enough that there was someone at the second table who gave me a franc; after that, everyone all down the line bought a card. Nobody took any further notice of me; that relieved me—I mean, I didn't exactly look like a globetrotter and didn't care for any indiscreet questions. In any case, not like that right at the start. Later on, I suppose, I taught myself to deal with them.

By the time I left the cafe, I had enough money to go over and get a shave, redeem my backpack from the checkroom, and get myself a bite to eat. Success right from the start.

I didn't feel like staying in Nice any longer than absolutely necessary and in the afternoon I began walking out along the coastal road.

8

It wasn't quite so amusing as I'd imagined. The backpack was damned heavy, the straps cut into me and my back became sore, the cars drove by me incessantly and forced me to walk way out onto the shoulder, which was full of holes and stones. In addition, of course, I hadn't been in bed at night and was tired and sleepy. Actually, of course, it was supposed to be beautiful there on a road like that along the Mediterranean, but the dust and heat ruined your ability to see something like that. Besides, you quickly get tired of looking at palms and agave and after a while you lose interest in the fact that the sea is blue—I mean, it's got to have some color and one's just as good as the next.

I was inside all the cafes on the way, but I didn't sell more cards than could just pay for the wine I drank. When I got to Cagnes sur mer,* I decided to spend the night there; I found a room at Madame Rose's up at the top of the mountain, and after I'd washed, changed socks, and gotten something to eat, I felt life was grand—now I'd finally found my niche, I could be a vagabond and enjoy freedom's blessings and still I had a kind of job, a legitimate occupation. I wanted to roam around the world like that. Damn it that I hadn't thought of that a little sooner.

My importance didn't really dawn on me until the next morning when a Swedish painter I met down in the cafe wanted my autograph and offered me a Pernod; in return, I told him some hair-raising stories from my globetrotting life. He wanted me to write articles for the newspapers about my experiences; I happened to think of Schmidt and said that modesty forbade. Let others lay themselves and their lives bare for people to contemplate, I said, and let them get paid for it—I just wish to carry out my project, the trip around the world on foot; afterward I want to buy myself a little cottage on the moor and live there with my woman and my children.

This way of looking at things impressed both him and myself and by the time I left Cagnes, I was in splendid spirits: now I'd finally found an attractive way of living and I had a goal to look forward to. Especially this stuff about the modest moorland cottage as an objective for the widely travelled globetrotter appealed to me—I wanted to cultivate the heather and eat coarse bread.

After I'd been in a series of cafes in Antibes without having sold a card, I pondered whether that wasn't a good idea to supplement my income by writing articles—I could buy myself a camera and market the material to the three leading Scandinavian papers; that way I could get out of these disgusting begging calls at the cafes, which were the sole dark spot in my existence. A fountain pen and a camera would be my weapons; I decided to carry out these plans as quickly as possible: this way I'd be able to earn a lot of money with a trip around the world, and maybe a nice little villa out on the Øresund* some place near Tårbæk* was a more pleasant goal to look forward to than the moorland cottage.

The card sales were poor and in Juan les Pins* I decided to go into the water. While I was lying on the beach after my swim eating peanuts, I thought through my plans more closely and felt good, as if I'd won the big prize in the lottery. I was a lucky son of a gun, a lucky dog: now I was lying here in the world's loveliest bay surrounded by the world's most famous people eating peanuts; I love peanuts—I believe they called them cacahuet* there. The man next to me explained that that nice gray-haired gentleman who was doing exercises on the beach was Chaplin. I was convinced that it was a lie, but still I enjoyed the feeling. It was a wonderful afternoon.

The next day it rained and since a bus to Cannes came by, I took it: after all, it wasn't on the road that anything ever happened and it wasn't on the road that I'd sell my cards. Nobody'd be cheated because I rode part of the way.

When I got to Cannes it was still raining and the sidewalk

cafes were filled with people. I was a big hit, sold a lot of cards, until a man took me aside and advised me to get out of town as quickly as possible—the police didn't allow that kind of thing in town and I risked being caught at any moment. I took the bus to St. Tropez.*

I'd now gotten accustomed to riding and the following days I rode from town to town. I was earning good money and bought myself a pair of high boots and a suitcase. When I got to a town, I rented a room at a cheap hotel right away, put on the boots, filled the backpack with crumpled up newspapers and went to the cafes. It was senseless for the backpack to be any heavier than necessary; on the other hand, I didn't look like a globe-trotter without it and it had to be full to look impressive.

I painstakingly took care that the boots didn't get polished—the dustier they were, the easier it was to sell the cards. In Toulon* there was a busybody of a chambermaid who'd polished them till they sparkled and looked absolutely new; she was very surprised to see how furious I got about it, and was cold as ice when I later tried to mollify her with an amiable remark. In order to get them to look like globetrotter boots again, I had to find a puddle on the outskirts of town and bespatter them, to the great astonishment of several boys who were standing there watching.

By the time I got to Marseille I was getting tired of being a globetrotter. It annoyed me, when I thought about what an honorable and difficult mission it actually was to go around the world on foot, that people in the cafes treated me haughtily and flung 50 centimes at me as if I were some kind of beggar. I mean, they couldn't know that I didn't walk all the time and that the rest of the story was a lie, and so they should've treated me with respect and interest. An American woman who'd come to Marseille to eat bouillabaisse,* became interested in me and I lived with her for a week in a villa she'd rented on La Corniche.* When I couldn't stand her any more after that week and left the villa one morning, I'd lost my desire to act the part of a globe-trotter and moved out to the Scandinavian seaman's home, where, after a few days, I was given an offer to hire on on a

Swedish steamer. I had the choice between taking the job or leaving the seaman's home and chose the latter, went to the consulate, and talked them into giving me a ticket to Paris. However, it turned out to be impossible to get it refunded any way except selling it to a discharged ordinary seaman for half price.

So I had to bring myself to go on with the globetrotting no matter how much I hated to do it.

Sixth Chapter

1

To be honest, I don't remember how long I was a globetrotter, but it was a long time, probably for most of a year, and when I stopped, I'd been around most of France. Some places I did really well and I really felt like taking these friendly towns in one more time, but of course that's the flaw with the globetrotter existence—that you can't go to a town more than once.

I think that's the way it must have been more or less right after the period when I became a smuggler in Sweden; in any case, there can't have been a long time in between. I'd gotten to Liverpool on an Italian freighter, but hadn't been in England for many months before I was caught by the police. That was in Hull and got me a three-week stay in jail. Naturally it was the consul who was to blame for the whole thing. You wouldn't believe that Danish consuls exist to support Danish subjects. This consul here was an Englishman who could speak a little Swedish; I tried to get him to give me a ticket to Esbjerg on one of The United's ships; I could have managed to sell it as easy as pie to someone or other—there's always a bunch of Scandinavians travelling that route. I was pretty down on my luck, had been walking the streets for a couple of nights, and hadn't tasted real food for a long time.

This consul was hard and unkind. I showed him a letter from my mother in Hobro*: I had to go home right away—father had been taken to the hospital and the doctors feared the worst. But he was deaf to all pleading—couldn't approve a ticket for me. I implored him not to prevent me from getting to my father's deathbed and became so stirred up over the man's pigheadedness that for a short while I myself was on the verge of believing that I had a dying father in Hobro. I feel this consul was exceptionally malicious—I mean, the story *could* have been true, there wasn't the slightest reason why it couldn't have been true.

But that's the way the consuls are. Even though he was probably one of the worst of the kind. Besides, he was distrustful. People of an unrefined character are as a rule distrustful. When I kept waving the letter from my mother, he demanded to see the envelope. That was a malicious way to treat a Danish seaman whose father was dying, and I admit that I became indignant. I asked him whether he thought I was lying. And I asked him since when it had become custom that people who sought the consulate's aid were branded as swindlers from the outset. Wasn't an insinuation like the one implied by his question about the envelope really the same as accusing me of being a swindler.

Naturally I didn't have any envelope. Where in the world should I have come by it. If you could come by it just as easily as you could go to the post office and write yourself a letter, there'd be nothing to it. The envelopes were always the weak point and you always had your work cut out for you convincing the consuls that it'd gotten lost. Besides, as a rule it's safer to get indignant. And it's never hard to lose your temper with a consul, especially when you start thinking about the fact that of course it *could* be a real letter you're showing him. Practically speaking, it's impossible to get yourself an envelope: it has to be written in the same handwriting as the letter, and, besides, the postal service stamp shows how old it is. On special solemn occasions I've gotten an acquaintance in Denmark to write such a letter and send it to me, but, for one thing, it's very complicated, and, for another, of course it quickly becomes out of date. I mean, your father can't be lying on his deathbed like that for years. And when you've had such trouble getting the letter, then, of course, you'd like to be able to use it more than once.

This consul wasn't a refined human being. When I said I was going to write to the Foreign Ministry and complain about him, he told me to scram and said that if I ever came back, he'd call the police. That's a free and easy way of looking after Danish subjects' interests.

There was a Dane living in Hull who had a tea room. He was from Roskilde* and was considered to be a clever man. He looked at the letter from my mother for a long time and said that he'd certainly take care of that matter—I should just go to the consul, who was a good friend of his. I said that I'd gone to the consul and been turned down. That didn't matter, said the tea-room man; in fact he'd call him—they were old friends—it was safe for me to go up there.

Under these circumstances I didn't take the risk into account—I've always trusted influence blindly; if you've got connections, everything's possible. When I returned to the consul's, two detectives were standing there waiting for me—I didn't get to see the consul at all. That was high-minded, wasn't it.

I was locked up for a week before they could pull themselves together and mount an interrogation. That was against the law, but the law isn't for the poor. Except when they violate it. Then, however, in fact it's mainly for the poor. Of course, under the circumstances I didn't understand a bit of English—you can't expect the lamb to put its own head on the block. The tea-room man acted as an interpreter; if there's money to be earned on a poor seaman, they'll be there, all right. Naturally, the consul was there too. The barristers were wearing wigs and gowns and I was a bit impressed that this whole apparatus had been staged for my sake.

I was charged with vagrancy.* They wouldn't believe that I'd come to Liverpool on an Italian freighter, especially since I couldn't remember the name of the boat. If you tell the truth, you don't have any chance of being believed. They kept cross-examining me on this point and since I was afraid that the time limit for the investigation would be extended, I decided to give them a story. I said that I could just as well confess sooner than later how in reality I'd gotten to England and if I hadn't said it right away, it was to cover up for the people who'd helped me. The truth was that a French fishing boat called *Pourquoi non** that was going to Dover had taken me along because I asked nicely and paid; I didn't think it was illegal since, after all, I had my passport. I answered the question as to why my passport hadn't been stamped by saying that passports hadn't been checked on board. The judge asked whether I really didn't know that people were required to be in possession of a certain sum of money to be allowed to set foot on English soil. I admitted that

I hadn't had any idea, but, to be on the safe side, I informed them that I'd had 700 francs on me when I went ashore. Since they wanted to know where I had the money from, I readily told them that I'd signed off on an American four-master in Le Havre, that the ship had gone into dock after an extraordinarily hard voyage around Cape Horn. To make it more lively, I added that the cook had been knocked overboard by a breaker in the Straits of Magellan, that he'd been my best friend, and that I couldn't understand that I'd never see him again.

The whole courtroom was moved and when I saw the effect my humble statements had had, I myself got tears in my eyes. That way they forgot to ask why I didn't have a discharge book and the case was quickly closed on the basis that I was deported and was to be sent home at the first opportunity.

2

It took two weeks before there was passage available to Esbjerg and during that time I was held in custody. I sat in a cell together with a beachcomber, a pickpocket, and a soldier, who had deserted, in full uniform. We really had a very enjoyable time; especially the soldier was full of humor: he turned his uniform jacket inside out, put it on backwards, and wrote in chalk across the back: "Jesus died for you." After that he put on a serious face and did a routine as a Salvation Army soldier—I've never seen better. And I've seen many of that kind of routine—the underworld can't stand the Salvation Army. I mean, it's odd, all right, that it's precisely the people the Salvation Army's set up to look after who can't stand it and the rich people who support it with money and think it's an excellent institution. I've never yet met a vagabond who could stand the Salvation Army. That's why that kind of vaudeville act the soldier performed inspires cheering on the outskirts of towns,* while respectable people say that they ought to be a little ashamed of themselves, that you mustn't mock that kind of thing, and so on.

The soldier did his stuff well—we were lying flat on our backs with laughter on our plank beds till we heard the keys rattling, the door being opened, and the prison guard shouting who the hell did we think we were. The soldier was from London and in private life was the son of a tavern-keeper in the East End. Of course he still was, but it's my opinion that when people become soldiers, all that kind of stuff stops—then they're just soldiers. When you see a company of soldiers march down a street, you don't think about the fact that they're a bunch of tailors, burglars, wholesale merchants' sons, night club waiters, YMCA officials, and vagabonds—they're just soldiers, who look totally alike, and maybe there isn't that big a difference among them either when push comes to shove.

The pickpocket didn't have any special social talents—he could wiggle his ears and sing "Inky pinky parlez vous."* He was very melancholy and sat most of the time biting his nails, the tramp could produce a tune by hitting himself on the head, and I was interesting because I was a foreigner, but otherwise I wasn't a real hit because I wore glasses. Naturally I told them some of my experiences, but they didn't really want to believe that a man with glasses could experience such things.

If we got too bored, we'd bang on the walls or scratch the paint off the plank beds. There was a toilet bowl in the cell; when we thrust the water out of it with the brush—by the way, all the prisoners did that every time it was used—you could talk to the prisoners in the other cells by sticking your head all the way down in the bowl and shouting.* However, you got tired of it—it was a strenuous position—and during our exercise in the prison yard we could chat with one another as much as we damn pleased. We had exercise in the prison yard twice a day and all the prisoners were in the yard at the same time. After the interrogations and hearings the bailiffs would collect all the cigarette butts that were lying around in the ashtrays, take them down into the yard, and hand them out to those of us who didn't have money for extra provisions; there were fine brands among them—the barristers sure know what they're smoking—many times you got a cigarette that only a puff or two had been taken from.

3

Then finally one day I was led into the office where they gave me the things that had been confiscated at the time of my arrest—my suspenders and what I'd had in my pockets—and a detective came for me to take me out to the ship. I was a little disappointed that the trip took place on a trolley; I'd been told that such transports usually take place by car and I'm very fond of riding in cars. Maybe the detective wanted to save the United Kingdom that expense or he pocketed the money himself.

When we got on board the ship, which was lying in the middle of the dock after having been hauled* out there, the officer wanted the captain to lock me in detention till we'd gotten out onto the water, but he refused and they outright quarreled over it; I heard the skipper say that here on board he was the highest authority and that he didn't take orders. I was touched by the skipper's attitude, but when we'd gotten out of the harbor, I realized that it wasn't for my sake he'd cut the policeman down to size. As he passed me on the way to his cabin, he snarled at me: Damn it all—that we have to have such rabble on board.

4

That's not the way I'd dreamt of returning to Copenhagen, and I hadn't been in town more than two days before I decided to get away again. I took the ferry to Malmö* and tramped up through Sweden.

In Norrköping* I got a job as an agent selling lace to private individuals. It actually went very well; after a while I got experience in chatting with the girls—little audacious compliments sometimes meant more than the quality of the merchandise. It was as a lace salesman that I went to Nykøping* and met old man Hellstrøm, who was one of the funniest people I've ever known. He lived by going to taverns with a big sketchbook under his arm and drawing people's portraits. His secret was that he could make people look more attractive without causing the likeness to suffer.

The old man's nickname was *the horse frightener*. He'd gotten it because he was afraid of horses. Scared not in the usual way, but mortally afraid. He'd shake all over and couldn't say a word. Even if it was a gentle old hack that was standing securely tethered in a field and didn't even bother to turn its head to look at him. We lived in the same hotel and had little Dutch treats up in the room. He was an expert at drinking and was offended by his not having succeeded in drinking me under the table. One day he'd apparently decided that it was now or never. We'd been at the alcohol monopoly company* restaurant and had dinner with lots of schnapps and strong beer; there we fell in with a travelling salesman dealing in photographic enlargements and a metal worker who was on the tramp.* All four of us decided to go back to the hotel room and continue the party.

When we got up to the room, we began playing twenty-one and drinking schnapps. Old man Hellstrøm was keeping an eye on me and getting more and more rattled by my still not getting drunk. While I was in the bathroom, he put ashes and a nail file in my beer. I'd been up against that trick before: if you drink a glass of beer that's been prepared that way, you get so sick that you want to die; you vomit nonstop and it takes several days before you're the same again. I saw right away what'd happened to the beer and said to him that I didn't think it was nice of him to treat a poor man that way. He got furious and said damn it all I was lying through my teeth. The metal worker jumped up from his chair and said that if it was true, the old man would get a beating. And if it was a lie, he'd teach all damned Danes what it meant to lie about an honest Swede. He was one of those who love to fight and couldn't hide his delight over the fact that, regardless of who was right, there was a row in the air. I took off my glasses and thought there was going to be a brawl.

And there was. Good lord, what a brawl. The photography salesman sniffed my beer glass and said that there were ashes in it. At the same moment the metal worker rushed at the old man, yanked at his artist's wig, and gave him a black eye. He had a splendid wig, the old man; he said himself that without it he couldn't sell one picture.

The old man fell over against the table, which went down with glasses, bottles, and everything. After that he sat down on his ass in between the beer spots and pieces of broken glass. The photography salesman was going to intervene, said that brutality was un-Nordic, and suggested that instead we give the old man a real spanking. The first thing it resulted in was the salesman's also getting a black eye, but when the idea had reached all the way into the metal worker's skull, he became pensive and came to the conclusion that it was actually an excellent idea.

We pulled the old man's pants off and used his own belt as an instrument of punishment. He howled and wailed, but the metal worker was not about to miss out on the amusement and the old man's skinny backside got one red stripe after the other.

Naturally it didn't go off totally calmly, and before we knew it, the room was filled with people trying to intervene. It turned into an enormous brawl. I was standing with the hotel porter's head under my arm punching him in the ribs when I heard the police car. I burst out of the room, ran upstairs one floor, and hid in a bathroom.

It wasn't till about an hour had gone by that I ventured out, walked down the service stairs, went out into the yard, and that way managed to escape the deportation from the kingdom of Sweden I was sentenced to a couple of years later anyway.

5

By now it was winter and since it was mainly in the area surrounding the cities I was supposed to sell my lace, the job was really hard all right. In Valdemarsvik* I rented a chair sled* to get moving faster. It's a chair on two runners; you stand behind the chair with one foot on one runner and with the other foot you push off. My sample case was strapped down on the chair. I got out to a small community safely where I did a good business, and after I'd eaten dinner, I set off on the way home. It was dark and the roadway was covered with ice. After hard slogging I'd reached the top of a hill and now I was really about to enjoy the rest down the hill—I straightened my back and breathed. Before I knew it, I was going tremendously fast—it was lovely, it would help me a good piece of the way up the next hill. But when the speed kept increasing and there was no sign that I was at the foot of the hill yet, I began to get nervous. All of a sudden the road made a turn; I didn't see it before the border of the forest sprang up right in front of me and I was able to realize that I wasn't on the roadway any more. I turned the chair sled so that I slid off and nearly toppled over. I made it, but I'd gotten scared. The chair sled continued storming downward and the hill didn't appear to have any end. If the road had at least been straight, but it made the most dreadful curves. I'd begun to ponder letting myself fall down—in any case that would've been better than smashing my head against a tree—but the speed by now had gotten so wild that I was afraid of breaking my neck. A moment later the chair sled left the roadway on its own initiative and tore over a plowed field, did a couple of somersaults, and hurled me on my head into a juniper bush.

I was pretty battered, but was still able to hobble across to a house, where there was a light, about a half-mile away. I was certain that I'd suffered terrible internal injuries and admired myself a little for not having remained lying there listlessly, but instead having overcome the pains and dragged myself off across the fields. When I got over to the cabin, the people would have to take care of me. Presumably I'd be taken to a hospital, even though I was, of course, too weak for that to happen during the first few days. I'd lost my glasses and my cap, and the thought of the state of my crown jewels almost made me give up. I thought it was marvelous what a person's energy and will-power could achieve. Presumably I'd collapse on the doorstep of the house. I'd often read about badly wounded people whose will-power was so enormous they could force their maimed body to obey till it had been removed to safety, and I'd always been aware that I was one of those people who'd be able to pull off such a feat.

I collapsed on the doorstep of the house after having

knocked on the door with one final exertion. The farmhands came out, I heard their voices very faintly, and was aware that they carried me in and put me on a bed.

6

While I was lying in bed, it seemed to me that I was feeling somewhat better, but still I felt I had to say no thanks to a cup of coffee. The farmer had been out looking for the chair sled and the rest of my worldly goods; actually, of course, it didn't matter—now I'd probably never need them any more; my glasses were undamaged—I put them on. I made a present of all the lace samples to the farmer's daughter, who was so gentle and considerate when she tucked pillows down behind my back; when I didn't lie completely still, it hurt, and when I winced, she looked totally frightened.

Late in the evening the doctor came; I heard the car brakes squeal in front of the house. While he was examining me, I said to him that I preferred to hear the truth no matter what it might be.

The truth, young man, he said, is that there isn't the slightest thing wrong with you. You've gotten a couple of skin scrapes and black and blue marks, but for that matter you can get up right away. If you hurry, you can drive with me to Valdemarsvik—otherwise you'll probably topple over again with your chair sled. My fee is 15 crowns.

7

It was pretty unpleasant to say goodbye to the nice people who'd been convinced that I was going to die on them. I heard the daughter tittering before the car door was closed. On the way I got the doctor to lower his fee to 10 crowns and was allowed to owe it till the first.

I left Valdemarsvik the next morning and used the last of my money on a ticket to Stockholm, where, as far as I recall, I was the whole winter. I lived on something called Dannemora Street and lived by hawking door to door. All sorts of things. Needles, buttons, sewing thread, tapes, soap, silk ribbons, and all that kind of stuff. I lugged around a big tote bag from one staircase to the next; I was energetic and thrifty. I think it was the most honest period of my life. And the poorest. In spite of everything, of course, I was, after all, my own master, and actually I didn't have anything against being virtuous as long as I wasn't ordered to do it. So it really wasn't especially entertaining.

And when spring came, I cleared out. Sold the bag and the stock on hand and tramped out on the road. Northward. Gävle, Sundsvall, Umeå, Skellefteå, Haparanda.* I was zooming and took the distances in record time, hailed cars on the road, and rode as a stowaway on freight trains. I didn't actually have anything I was chasing after, but it shook the Stockholm stairway dust off me, so to speak, and gave me a sense of accomplishing something, of moving forward. Incidentally, the rushing and my ambition as a vagabond led to my nearly breaking my neck between Härnösand and Örnsköldsvik.* I'd asked the tramps in Härnösand when a freight train would be going to Örnsköldsvik, as if it were the most natural thing in the world for me to take the next train. It was really something of a game of chance to take a train, and you often had to let several trains go by before you succeeded in getting up into a brake compartment without being seen and hiding there. And naturally it annoyed them that I took it for granted that I'd take the first train and that I asked about the departure time the same way a tourist asks at a travel agency. I mean, it was in fact precisely to annoy them that I did it.

That's why they decided to take revenge and their revenge nearly cost me my life. As the time for my departure approached, they said they'd accompany me down to the rail yards to wave goodbye. Naturally I protested, said that it was touching of them, but that I couldn't accept it—they shouldn't waste their precious time on me, and so on. But I couldn't shake them off and we were quite a good-sized and sensational crew by the time we got to the rail yards five minutes before that train's departure they'd given me the information about.

We heard a train coming from the south; it was approaching very fast and rolled into the station. There's your train, said one of them, give my regards to your aunt in Örnsköldsvik.

I don't think these congenial ruffians could tell by looking at me what I was feeling. It was a nasty practical joke they'd played on me: the train was a passenger train, an express train. Every honest prince of the road knows that it's impossible to ride as a stowaway on an express train—there aren't any freight cars and that's why there aren't any brake compartments.

My honor as a vagabond was at stake: if I was made a fool of, all of Sweden's highways would know it within a month, and I wouldn't be able to show my face anywhere without having to take that lying down. I looked at the train. There was a possibility I could jump up on the tender, where there was a little narrow iron landing I could stand on, and an iron bar I could hold on to.

When the train got going, I flung away the cigarette and hopped on. I didn't get time to look at their faces—those are powerful trains: in the course of a few seconds they're in full swing. I had enough to do holding on tight. It was insane of me to risk my life in order to impress that ragtag riff-raff. The express trains travel at more than 60 m.p.h., and tomorrow it'd say in the *Norrskensflamman** that the body of a vagabond with glasses had been found a few miles north of Härnösand. Yeah, the glasses, in a second they'd been blackened by soot from the engine so I couldn't see a bit, and I didn't dare let go with one hand and put them in my pocket. There was nothing else for me to do but hold on tight, close my eyes, grit my teeth, and just think about this one thing: holding on tight.

If the railway line had been straight, the risk would've been smaller, but it went into curves, into tremendous windings around cliffs and lakes. On these curves the roadway was built with a banking* so the train didn't need to slow down. When I was standing on the inside of the curve, I was pressed in against the tender and was able to loosen my grip, but when I was standing on the outside, it was as if a huge magnet was going to suck me out into the air, constantly more and more, until the train once again began to straighten itself out.

On the biggest curve I was standing on the outside, and if it'd taken just a few seconds longer before the train straightened itself out, I would've been flung off; I sensed my fingers slowly loosening their grip on the iron bar, saw my hands slowly opening because of the pull my body was exerting. I wasn't thinking that I was going to die now, didn't see my life pass before my eyes and all that stuff: my sole thought was to hold on tight, hold out—sooner or later the curve would have to be over with. When the pull was at its highest, my cap flew off—that gave me such a shock that I was nearly flung off with it.

When the curve was past, the train braked. Maybe my flying cap was the reason that they'd discovered me. Long before the train had come to a stop, the stoker stuck his head out of the locomotive and bawled me out in a very irritated and impolite way. Since the speed had slowed down so much that I dared to, I jumped off, rolled down the slope, and ran away from the railway embankment in order not to be arrested. By the time I'd gotten a little ways away and turned around, I saw the locomotive engineer waving his fist at me. I sat down, dried off my glasses, and pretended that it wasn't me he was waving his fist at. A little later they moved on.

8

It was on this trip north that I had one of the strangest experiences I've ever had. I'm actually not happy about telling about it—the times I've done so, people have put their index finger on their temple and buzzed like a bee.* Tonight I won't think twice about it, and maybe you'll believe it.

While we're on the subject of trustworthiness, I'd like to repeat what I said before. I'm not trustworthy. Quite apart from the advantages I've gotten by it, I've always felt a certain pleasure in telling people something that was pure fabrication. Even as a child I was prone to it and was always severely punished for it. I distinctly remember one day I'd been in Østre Park* playing with my buddies and came home too late. I really always did that, after a while people took it for granted that I wasn't able to be punctual, and they hardly noticed it. But that day I ran into father on the stairs and he asked me where I'd been. I told him and father was about to keep going downstairs when it occurred to me to tell him that one of the boys in the park had a horse that wasn't any bigger than the dog of the woman who had a business running people's laundry through a mangle. The dog of the woman who ran the mangle business was a fox terrier.

Father turned around down on the landing and looked at me, furious. Now, you know, you're lying again, boy, he said. I avowed that I'd told the truth, I'd seen the horse with my own eyes, played with it, and pulled it by the tail. It wasn't bigger than what would fit in father's overcoat pocket.

Now my father got totally furious, leaped up the stairs and caught hold of me, shook me, and shouted out so the house could hear it. He dragged me into the entrance hall. Naturally I howled—that was usually the means of getting him to stop—and admitted that that business with the horse was just something I'd made up. Then he wanted to know why I'd done it, and even if I'd gladly wanted to, I wouldn't have been able to explain it to him. I didn't know. He kept pressing me. Now I want to know why you tell those kinds of stories, he shouted. I was at my wits' end; he dragged me into the bedroom and ordered me to pull my pants down. Now I'll teach you once and for all to stop your cock-and-bull stories, he said.

In order to avoid a beating I tried to think up an explanation—I said that it was because I'd always wished for a little dog that looked like a horse, and that the teacher had said that in Australia they had little horses like that cavorted in the mountains and lived on berries and earthworms. I didn't say it to irritate him—I myself thought it sounded credible—but father got blue in the face, flung me down on the bed, and thrashed away at me until mother knocked on the door and shouted: Barnabas, you're gonna kill the boy.

Out in the entry hall he shouted that now he'd be late because of me, to boot—he was going to a meeting on pedagogy.

Pedagogy was his hobby horse. And he added that my brothers and sisters weren't allowed to talk to me for a week and that I wasn't allowed to have any dinner, but instead would be put to bed. Then I could lie there and think about what my untruthfulness had led to.

I remember that I cried myself to sleep. When my brothers and sisters came in to go to bed, they didn't dare talk to me, but pulled back my blanket to see the stripes that were evenly distributed across my back and my thighs. Then I wound up crying again. In general I cried a lot as a child; in school the teacher could make me cry just by looking at me.

9

I think you understand that even though my life has turned out the way it has, there's no reason to doubt any of what I'm sitting here telling you this evening. Just as it's been a pleasure for me to make up a story now and then, this evening it's been a relief for me not to need to conceal anything, not to distort anything, not to be forced to keep back anything.

I can do that all the better since presumably we won't be having anything to do with each other again, and whatever opinion you'll form of me won't matter. I realize that it won't be very pretty; I've told you the brutal truth about my life—how many people could do that and still retain the fine reputation they've succeeded in bluffing their way to. It's not a pretty and uplifting tale you're getting for the helping hand you've given me, and I wonder what pleasure you'd get from having a rigmarole like that palmed off on you; isn't the truth about a wretched human being's defeat when confronted with difficulties just as interesting, especially when the poor devil's sitting right across from you and really exists. I'm no hero, I doubt altogether that heroes exist. And if any really do exist, I wouldn't care to know them. I'm a perfectly ordinary person who's gone to seed because I had a good upbringing, because I had to rebel against the desert the adults made my life into, because the urge to rebel never left me, was never satisfied, and despite everything I could never really turn into anything because I was raised into a slave existence and was afraid of responsibility when the chips were really down.

I don't expect you to feel sorry for me—I can assure you I don't give a good goddamn—but I do expect you to believe me. People are filled with stories, one more profound and phoney than the next; what I've told you this evening is just a story about a fellow human being whose life was made a mess of. And of course a human being has only one life. For other people his life is just a detail in the picture of the world, but for him it is the world.

If I'd at least gotten off with just getting a beating as a child, if I'd been so lucky that the morality that was beaten into me hadn't been so firmly rooted, then maybe I could've saved my life. But it was firmly rooted and it ruined the game for me the couple of times I had a chance. That morality is good enough for the person who stays in the box—in fact, it's even a support—but for a person who's cast out into conditions that deviate from the normal, morality's a hindrance. It's very pleasant for others—especially for the ones who own something it's reassuring that people are moral—but for people themselves it's a weakness in the struggle for existence.

My life as a smuggler in Sweden could've been my chance if I'd been strong enough to take it, but what can you expect of a parish deacon's son with glasses. Well, before I became a smuggler, incidentally, that, of course, was when I had that strange experience I began telling you about. It was pretty far up north, I think up around Luleå,* that it took place. I'd been marching north for many days, as if the devil were on my heels—it gave me, so to speak, an outlet for something, a feeling that I was doing something. It was a long way between the farms there, and I didn't get much to eat those days; I also didn't care—it was a relief to see the countryside become less and less civilized, and in a pinch I could really do without food for days at a time. Mainly I slept outside or in barns, which were located far away from the dwelling houses, so I didn't need to ask permission and avoided having to say thanks when I went on the next morning.

10

Sometimes it's happened to me, when I was going to walk across a street and the traffic was shaping up in a very definite way, that I felt I'd experienced the situation once before. You know, no two situations are totally alike—there's always a detail that diverges. And it's especially the detail you recognize. First comes a green truck with a dented front fender, then a bicycle messenger with teeth like tusks, then a taxi whose driver is buttoning his jacket while he's driving and swerves because a crazy fox terrier's fooling around on the roadway. A combination like that you won't see twice in your life, and still it's happened to me several times that I've been able to say with certainty that I've seen this picture before. As if I'd seen it in dreams. Once I came to a little Swedish town called Laholm,* and as I stepped out of the train station onto the street, that feeling came over me. I knew that town, despite the fact that I'd never been there before. It was as if I'd lived my childhood there and were now returning home. When I turned a corner, I knew exactly what it looked like. If you'd asked me what it was going to look like around the next corner, presumably I wouldn't have been able to answer; I can only say that what I saw was so self-explanatory. When I say that it was like recognizing the town of your childhood, that's not quite right either, because the details, which were a part of the picture I recognized, were something especially for that moment I got to the town. A girl with yellow braids who was coming out a door, a butcher who was standing and talking to two ladies dressed in black, a piece of paper that the wind had swept along the street.

I don't know how to explain that kind of experience; maybe it's just an expression of the state of mind you're in. I've heard that after strenuous marches soldiers can experience something similar, and if I'm telling you about what happened to me back then up in northern Sweden, it's because that way you'll get a clearer picture of the person who, by ordinary notions, I suppose, behaved in a pretty deranged way.

If I've decided to speak my mind about my life, it's not because I want you to think that I'm a bad person. I myself have never been able to view myself that way. What is a bad person altogether? People act based on their feelings, their morals, and their intellect, and they're not responsible for any of them. When I think back, there are certainly many cases where today I'd have acted differently, but only because today I have more experience and a different morality. I've always done what I regarded as right. Presumably everyone does. When you really have time to think it over, when your feelings don't dictate quick action. Back then in northern Sweden, I must have been like a soldier after a strenuous march of many days, physically and mentally exhausted. I mean, I don't remember any more what was going on in me back then, what thoughts, what ideas I had, and it seems to me that my flight from Stockholm and northward looks pretty idiotic, but I remember this episode and maybe it can explain a little what I was like in those days. I mean, you often feel that people do foolish or loathsome things, but looked at with their own eyes, they absolutely can't act differently. I mean that's why they do it.

Briefly the incident was as follows: I hailed a small, red sports car and hitched a ride. The driver didn't say a word to me, just stopped the car, opened the car door, and let me get in and sit down. He was a strange little man with a beard several days old, ferrety little eyes, slovenly, and repulsive. One minute I pegged him as being a criminal on the run in a stolen car, the next as insane, and then as a novelist. He sat bent over the steering wheel, didn't look to the left or the right, didn't say a thing, and drove at a speed that was never below 50 m.p.h. The car didn't weigh much and the road was bad, winding, and full of potholes. A woman who was standing on the road with a basket tried to stop us by waving. He stopped and backed up without saying a word, put up the backseat, and let her climb into the car. She asked if she could get a lift to town, but didn't get any answer; he just stepped on the gas and we raced on.

When we got to town, he stopped. While the woman was getting out, she thanked us effusively, but before she managed to finish speaking, he cut her off by saying she had to pay two crowns for the trip. She was totally overwhelmed and couldn't say a word. When he began to curse her up and down, she hurried up and paid.

A little further down the road we stopped at a gas tank and bought gas. He paid with the lady's two-crown piece after having gotten confirmation that I didn't have any money. A moment later we drove on.

After a while I was certain that the man was crazy, but on the other hand I couldn't have cared less what might happen. Late in the night we came to a ferry. The ferrying took place on a raft of logs that the ferryman hauled across the stream by pulling at an iron wire that was stretched from one shore to the other. There was no light on in the ferry house. The madman drove the car right out onto the raft and put his finger on the electric horn until a light was turned on. A moment later an old man tumbled out the door without having had time to get dressed.

Not a word was uttered while we were ferried across, the motor hummed faintly, the water of the stream lapped across the raft, and the wire creaked every time the old man pulled.

As soon as we reached land, the madman stepped on the gas; the car, as it were, leaped ashore, and the noise of the motor drowned out the ferryman who was shouting at us because he hadn't gotten any money.

11

After a while I'd gotten into a strangely apathetic state. Mile after mile we raced northward. Once we came to a big hill, which the car for some reason or other couldn't take; almost at the top the car came to a stop and a little bit later began going down backwards; I don't think he used the brakes; in any event, we whizzed backwards down the hill at the same speed that respectable people drive forwards on a level road. When the car had gotten as far up the hill at the bottom as it was going to, he started the motor and floored the gas pedal, shooting forward. We didn't reach the top of the hill this time either and had to go down again backwards, even more recklessly than the first time. He started again and we drove a quarter-mile backwards up the hill at the bottom before he decided to try again. This time we got up.

Far into the night we stopped and lay down to sleep on a grassy slope.

12

I woke up in the strangest way I've ever woken up. I woke up walking. I woke up very slowly, and quite gradually it dawned on me that I was walking on a highway. And I was still walking. Only when it completely dawned on me did I become wide awake and I stopped with a jerk.

It was late afternoon and I found myself on the outskirts of a village. I rooted through my pockets and found a cigarette butt, sat down on the side of the road, and tried to get a clear grasp on the situation.

Somewhat later an old man came leading a cow. I asked him where I was. He mentioned a name I wasn't familiar with. After he'd left again, I took out my map and tried to find the name. It was located two and a half miles down a byway.

I walked to the village and found a suitable house and asked for something to eat. I said I was going to Luleå and asked the way. The woman said I was going the wrong way, that I had to go back to the main road, half a Swedish mile* back in the direction I'd come from. I asked whether she'd seen a little red car. She explained that cars never came on this road, which was a dead-end and ended up by the new red houses near the woods.

In the evening I got back to the main road and turned north. After I'd been walking for ten minutes, I came to the place where we'd been lying and sleeping. There were still marks in the grass where we'd been lying and car tracks on the shoulder where the car had been standing. It was three miles from the place where I'd woken up.

Seventh Chapter

1

I became a smuggler by accident. It began completely innocently, one of the many small opportunities that lie along a person's path, one of the many insignificant breaches of the law that produced a little money and a little excitement. And maybe a little romanticism. I mean, it's been established once and for all that it's romantic to be a smuggler, and you really do feel the romanticism during the operation, maybe because you identify with the heroes in the smuggler tales you were brought up on. Why it should actually be more romantic to be a smuggler than to perform any other job whatsoever on this earth is something you begin to ponder when smuggling's not new any more, but a job that has to be done like anything else. There's a risk in smuggling as with anything else, and there's drudgery and damned toil as with anything else.

I'd gotten as far up as Kiruna.* It's Sweden's northernmost town, a miners' town, where there were always a dozen vagabonds, since it was, after all, a kind of last stop, and it's hard for people to make up their minds to turn around and return to the towns they just left.

It wasn't a big town—a collection of wooden houses and barracks, a few cafes, a billiard parlor. There were many Finns and Estonians among the miners, and on the streets you'd see Laplanders who came down from the mountains* to shop; day and night you heard the din of blasting and ore transports from the mountain *Kirunavaara*;* and in the railway switchyards long lines of full dump cars and long lines of empty dump cars were standing; behind them was a lake with huge swarms of mosquitoes and millions of croaking frogs. I loafed around most of the day, lying up on the mountain and dawdling or sitting and hanging around the billiard parlor; in the evening I went out and begged a little food and money. At the billiard parlor sometimes I was able to earn a beer by picking up billiard pins.* Once in a while a vagabond came from Narvik* with his pockets filled with Norwegian cigarettes called *Teddy** that were in demand because a decent cigarette in Sweden cost a fortune on account of the tobacco monopoly.* Teddy cost 25 øre in Norway, and with the exchange rate the way it was back then, that was the equivalent of 15 Swedish øre. And you gladly gave 50 øre for a pack of Teddy. That's why it was a rule that everyone who came to Kiruna from Narvik took along whatever cigarettes they were able to have in their pockets.

Of course I couldn't stay in Kiruna the rest of my life and I didn't much feel like heading back south. So I had to go to Narvik. There were only two directions from Kiruna, north to Narvik and south to Gällivare.* I mean, the whole country was nothing but mountains and tundra. And since I didn't have any money, I had to walk. I could follow the rail line north; presumably I'd be able to scrounge up food and lodging with the railway officials who lived along the line. I couldn't stow away—the big dump cars, which were the size of an ordinary Danish freight car, were loaded to the top with iron ore.

I don't remember how long I was en route; I think it was a trip of 125 miles. Many places the roadway was covered to protect against snowdrifts or went through long tunnels. At these places it was smartest to go across the mountain, even though it was a long and arduous detour: the tunnels were narrow and the iron ore trains, which were electric, built up a tremendous head of steam. It would happen that some reindeer would be run over and the iron ore company would have to pay compensation to the Laplanders. The railway crews said that the Laplanders themselves chased the reindeer onto the track to get compensation.

Across the Norwegian border the mountain landscape turned wilder, the mountains were higher, the gorges deeper, steeper, and more rugged, and there were countless tunnels. Several places the track ran along the edge of a mountain with a dizzying chasm underneath, and when a train went past, I had to press myself up against the rock wall of the cliff. In a tunnel I'd dared to go into, I had to jump down into a ditch with ice-cold water, which reached up to my stomach; it was impossible to hear the trains before they were on top of you. Along the way I saw both eagles and bears, but I've been told so often that that was a tall story that I've now begun to doubt whether I'm remembering correctly.

When I reached Narvik it was so hot that people did nothing but walk around in bathing suits and eat *rømmekolle*.* Apart from the ones who were forced to be doing something. After I'd taken a look at the town and collected my thoughts, I began considering whether I should bum my way south through Norway or sail as a stowaway on an iron ore carrier to Antwerp. One might be just as good as the other: it's not so much a matter of where you are as how you feel. And damn it, people are alike wherever you go—they want to get you work and the police want to catch you and send you home; I mean, after all, you'd think that people'd be allowed to figure out for themselves what they want to do—there's nobody who asked to be put in the world.

After I'd been out snooping in the single-family residential neighborhood to find a suitable place to eat lunch, I ran into a man who said that a Danish engineer lived in a single-family house a little further up—I'd be able to recognize it by an ornamental balcony and by the fact that there was a girl always pottering about the garden. He added that these days she was going around in a bathing suit and that she was really a scrumptious girl with great breasts.

In my early days as a vagabond, whenever I was going to get supplies, I always went into the first place that came along. And in the beginning I always followed the advice I got. Now I was more careful. To begin with, of course, you'd like to get something decent to eat; second, you often have bad experiences when you follow the advice people give you. Third, countrymen are rarely the best people to go to.

When I found the villa with the ornamental balcony, I tried to figure out whether ii was a good eating place. Maybe you wouldn't believe that it's possible to see by looking at a house whether those are people who live well and are high and mighty, but it is. This one here didn't look so reassuring. People with ornamental balconies are generally snobbish and snobbish people are rarely generous. But maybe he'd bought the house and been too high and mighty to bother about redoing it. The garden was well-kept without being meticulous. Meticulous people are often petty. On the other hand there was a dog and I can't stand dogs.

Despite the fact that the man was a Dane and had a dog and ornamental balcony, I went in. Behind the house I ran into the girl in the swimming suit. She was lovely.

2

I can't stand manual labor. It's the kind of work that's paid the worst and for that reason despised the most. If you can see by a man's hands and clothes that he's never touched a tool, he's treated respectfully and politely. The more a man's appearance is marked by physical labor, the less consideration he's shown. I can't stand that people think they're doing a good deed when they get you a job doing manual labor. And I can't stand having to pretend to be glad about having gotten it. That's what I had to do with the engineer when he said that I could dig in his garden for a week.

If it hadn't been because it was so difficult to get away from Narvik, and if the girl in the swimming suit hadn't been there, I wouldn't have taken it.

In the following days I dug till the sweat was pouring out of me. The sun beat down and there wasn't a breath of air. I didn't do any more than was absolutely necessary, and still the sweat streamed down my body. I'd have preferred to have lain down in the shade under a bush and smoked a cigarette, but every evening the engineer inspected the area that'd been dug, and in contrast to so many other jobs, with digging it's impossible to give the impression that you've done more than you have. Of course, you can stress the difficulties the work involves, rocks in the ground, the heat, quack-grass roots, and so on—of course, not in such a way that you complain, God forbid, but as interesting circumstances associated with the work. I gave the engineer to understand that the difficulties with the work stimulated me, that adversity gave me energy.

The girl in the swimming suit was a relative he had in the house; unfortunately I didn't see much of her, just a glimpse now and then. I wanted to make an impression on her and began to get a little vain, I constantly found pretexts for going up to the house, washed myself and combed myself, cleaned my nails, and let my glasses stay in their case. In that heat it would've been natural to have only a pair of pants on, but since I'm narrow-shouldered and have long, thin arms, I endured the torture of working with a shirt on.

I used every occasion to get to talk to her, and since she was smiling and friendly on these occasions, I was certain that I'd surely conquer her if I just had enough time to do it. I intimated to her that I was no ordinary vagabond—the urge for adventure and manly exploits had driven me out; my father was a pastor and all doors were open to me if I just wanted to return home.

3

One evening when the engineer was at a meeting, she agreed to go for a walk with me. We walked a ways outside of town and sat down on a rocky knoll. At night the sun stood like a dim globe on the horizon; a pale light lay across the landscape and the sea* lay out behind the town. It was pleasantly cool and on my forearm I could sense the warmth from her body. When I put my arm around her shoulder, the fact that she was naked underneath her dress rushed through me like a fire. I forced her down and kissed her, her lips were shut tight, and she stiffened in my arms. As I was unbuttoning her dress at the neck and slipped it down over her shoulder, down over one breast, she freed herself and jumped to her feet.

I jumped to my feet too, but my heart was beating so fast I couldn't say a peep. She buttoned herself up at the neck, smoothed out her dress, and began to leave. When I caught up with her, I saw that she was smiling. A summer night like this is really a wondrous thing, she said. And added a bit later: But

I mean that's no reason why you can't behave yourself.

So she wasn't angry. But then what was she? Maybe she just wanted to make a fool of me. I considered whether I should get melancholy—sometimes that has a marvelous effect on women—but it came more naturally to me to be offended. That's why I didn't answer her, I didn't say a word at all on the way home, and when we reached the villa, I curtly said good night and went up to my room.

The next day I had come to the view that I could just as well give her up—there was something of a vampire in her—and I didn't feel like being a plaything. That day was tremendously long; I dug like a dog and didn't get up to the house a single time; I dug a huge area and didn't care whether it occurred to the engineer that I could easily have done somewhat more the previous days; I wanted to be done, get my money, and leave town. Maybe I'd buy Teddy-cigarettes with all the money and take them to Kiruna. Then later you could always see what you might come up with.

In the evening we sat out in the garden and drank coffee. The engineer told tall tales about back when he'd built a railroad in Persia* and I could sense that the girl was sitting and trying to figure out what I was thinking about; she probably wanted to try and manage to arrange for us to wind up talking to each other. But she wasn't going to vamp me; I said to the engineer that, of course, soon I'd really be done and that I'd thought about going to Spitsbergen* and getting a job there—did he know when a boat was leaving.

Nobody called me the next morning and after I'd washed and went down, no breakfast had been set out for me in the kitchen, as it usually was. Furious, I went through the living and dining rooms to ask her what she meant by that. I found her in the engineer's bedroom; his bed was still unmade and she was standing in a swimming suit at the window with a newspaper in her hand. I could see by the hair by her ears that she'd taken a bath and I asked her whether I was going to get breakfast. Make it yourself, she answered and began reading the newspaper. If it'd been her intention to make me mad, she succeeded: I took her roughly by the wrist and tore the newspaper away from her. She bent over to pick it up and, in order to prevent her from doing that, I brutally shoved her down onto the bed. Each time she tried to get up, I shoved her down again. When she finally made a violent attempt to get up, I twisted her wrist so she wound up lying down and I asked her whether she intended to make coffee for me or not. Suddenly I noticed that her muscles were limp; I loosened my grip on her wrist and saw she was crying. She turned her face away and burrowed it into the pillow; I stuck my hand under the back of her head, turned her face upward, and dried her tears with a corner of the sheet. The corners of her mouth quivered and when I bent down and kissed her, I got a salty taste on my lips from her tears. This time her mouth wasn't pursed, but soft and limp. When I pulled the swimming suit off her, she didn't resist.

4

The girl's name was Gurli and she was very sun-tanned, but where the swimming suit had been she was white; it looked so vivid as if she had socks on. We swore each other eternal faithfulness, and when I got my money three days later from the engineer and was going to leave, we agreed that every night precisely at the stroke of twelve we'd think of each other. Every night at twelve o'clock she'd say that a summer night was a wondrous thing, but that was no reason I couldn't behave myself, and every night at twelve o'clock I'd ask whether it was her intention to give me breakfast or not. Every night at twelve for the rest of our lives we'd think of each other, and if I got married, I'd think of her when I kissed my wife. And I said to her that I'd never be able to forget that it had looked as if she'd had on socks that morning on the engineer's bed.

Her name was Gurli and she answered my first letter with four pages of glowing love, my next one she answered with a postcard, and my third she didn't answer at all. And the first week I thought of her every night at twelve o'clock.

5

I spent all the money on Teddy-cigarettes and jumped on an ore-train that was going south at three in the morning. From Narvik to Kiruna the ore-cars run empty and the cars are so big that you can stand up in them without being seen. I was sitting with my big package between my knees thinking about the stories I'd heard about vagabonds who'd been killed riding in empty ore cars, because it happens that the floor of the car opens beneath you if the closing mechanism isn't handled right. The sun was standing like a dim globe on the horizon and the empty ore cars were making a hell of a racket. In addition I killed time figuring out how much money the cigarettes would bring in and how I was going to invest my capital afterward.

And when we'd gotten across the Norwegian border, the landscape changed: there were once again tundra and low mountains, and when I got up and looked over the top, once in a while I could see a glimpse of places I recalled from my walking trip. In addition, I was thinking about Gurli and was a little nervous, a little jealous about her living alone in the villa with the ornamental balcony with the engineer, who was her relative, but, after all, was surely only a human being.

When we got to Kiruna, I cleaned my glasses with one of the engineer's handkerchiefs and hopped down from the car with my big package.

6

And when I was lying in my good hotel bed in the little hotel by the railroad station, I happened to think about the girl I'd once known at a gardener's whose name was Guse and lived outside Hamburg. That was before I got glasses and she'd been white not only where her swimming suit is, but had been white all over her body. And just then I heard a clock strike twelve and I hurried up and thought of Gurli, who according to the schedule was now supposed to be lying in her bed up in Narvik thinking of me and saying that that was no reason why I couldn't behave myself. And right after that I once again happened to think of the girl in Hamburg who cried in such a way that the tears ran down into her ears, and maybe that night Guse's girl was thinking about me and maybe the girl in Narvik had forgotten the agreement about twelve o'clock. The film directors didn't know life: when a girl's lying in bed crying, the tears didn't run down along the root of her nose, but down into her ears. In *Porjus* I'd seen a Finn stabbed with a knife, and in the movies where people back then were knifed for next to nothing, I'd never seen a man knifed that way. Porjus is a little town west of Gällivare, where there's a big power station* and lots of raftsmen who get drunk every evening on Estonian moonshine, which is a yellowish, cloudy liquid and tastes like crap. There was a Finn who came into a little cafe down by the mountain stream and wanted to sell daggers with sheaths made of reindeer bone, and he hadn't been there but two minutes when a drunken rafter took offense at the way he was acting; they stood at the door saying nice words to each other and all of a sudden the Finn doubled over and fell on his knees like a Muhammadan praying to God. He said nothing but a long drawn-out oh and there was no one who'd seen a knife. The whole thing went quite peacefully and quietly; there was almost no one in the cafe who noticed it and the drunken rafter just went on his way. In the movies there's always a big stir the moment a person's going to be stabbed with a knife: the murderer waves the weapon about and the victim screams and when he finally gets the knife, it happens with a tremendous swing of the arm. In reality, something like that takes place so quickly and imperceptibly that it's not until long afterward that it dawns on you what happened. But when people go to the movies and pay to see a person stabbed with a knife, it's only fair that they want something for their money and if they don't get a close-up of the dagger in the man's stomach, they go home and say that it was a bad film. But that business with the tears in any case is wrong and girls who lie in bed and cry presumably don't do it any differently in Hollywood than anywhere else on the globe.

7

Without actually thinking about it, I became a wholesale smuggler.* After I'd sold the cigarettes, I had so much money that I was able to travel to Narvik as a passenger for a bigger shipment. I put the big package in an empty ore car and I myself rode on a ticket in the only passenger car that was part of that train. It went smoothly and every time I'd sold out, it was natural for me to set off for a new shipment. By virtue of my constantly bigger purchases I obtained a more advantageous price, and when I was in Narvik for the fourth time, I had a long conversation with my supplier in a little cafe, where we drank twelve bottles of bock beer and managed to make an arrangement, according to which an acquaintance of the tobacco dealer was supposed to put a consignment of cigarettes in an empty ore car whenever I made an order by letter. We were thorough, got ourselves a train schedule of the ore trains' departure, and agreed that he'd put a little cross on each side of the car he put the package in. That way I'd get out of travelling to Narvik every other minute, and, besides, sooner or later it'd attract attention if I was continuously shuttling between Kiruna and Narvik. Naturally I had to pay the tobacco dealer's acquaintance something for his trouble, but on the other hand I saved time and travel expenses and could leave it at making one nightly visit a week to Kiruna's rail yards and picking up my package in the ore car that had a little cross on the side. According to the train schedule, I knew exactly on the dot when our train was going to arrive and could stand by.

It went smoothly, and in fact just as arranging the transportation had gone automatically, organizing the sales went automatically too. There was a Norwegian seaman bumming around the cafes in Kiruna named Anton. He was smart enough that you didn't need to be afraid that he'd make blunders and he wasn't smart enough that you needed to be afraid that he'd stab you in the back and pull a fast one. He got a percentage of every package he sold and little by little he took over all the selling. The only thing I had to do was pick up the package at the rail yards, send the money to Narvik, and make sure to keep Anton supplied with merchandise. It went amazingly easily; I was the one who had it easiest and I was the one who earned the most.

Naturally it quickly became apparent that I had to undertake an expansion: I could import as much as was necessary, but there was a limit to what could be sold in Kiruna. That's why I went to Gällivare and found a man who could be in charge of sales there on the same terms as Anton: I'd send him the merchandise from Kiruna C.O.D.; that way I didn't need to be afraid that he'd pull some trick or cheat me out of the money. When I'd gotten dealers in Porjus and Malmberget* too, I decided to give Anton a fixed salary to pick up the packages at the rail yards whenever I informed him that a shipment would be coming. That way I had a freer hand to travel and managed to avoid the risk that was naturally involved in picking up the packages.

After I'd expanded my market to include Luleå and Piteå,* too, it turned out that there were problems involving the organization that I had to take a position on and solve. If my dealers earned too much, I might be running the risk that they'd start up on their own, and if they earned too little, they'd be dissatisfied. Since the sales possibilities weren't exactly the same in the various towns, I had to let their earnings vary, and since they presumably wouldn't care to hear that other people had better terms than they themselves did, I had to prevent them from getting to know one another. In some towns I had to appoint two dealers in order to keep their earnings down so they didn't get to be too strong for me and maybe take it into their heads to want to dictate to me the prices they wanted to offer. In addition, I had to take care of my own security, take care to keep in the background and be known by the fewest possible people.

I earned piles of money, outfitted myself from head to toe in Narvik, and always had a fat wallet on me. I bought new glasses with horn rims and an ornamental handkerchief with my initials.

My headquarters were in Kiruna, where I had a permanent room at the hotel near the train station, but as time went on I was constantly travelling in order to organize sales in the various towns.

8

And at that point in time I think I was happy. I didn't have much time to think this question over; I had my hands full and when I went to bed at night, I wanted it to be morning quickly so I could get cracking again. I was constantly expanding my territory and after a while cigarettes were being shipped from Narvik every day. I realized that with the extent the organization had acquired and the large number of people who were implicated after a while, sooner or later a clash with the authorities had to occur, and all my attention was directed at this danger. Sooner or later a dealer would be arrested—the point was to prevent this from leading to the exposure of the whole organization; in part by threats, in part by promises, I had to succeed in getting an arrested dealer to keep his mouth shut. In case of arrest I promised to pay the fines and take care of the person concerned when he got out again. On the other hand, I hinted that the organization was nationwide and that a betrayal wouldn't be amusing for whoever committed it. In spite of all the cautiousness, I had problems a couple of times and had to intervene quickly and brutally to cope with the situation. This intervention was so intensely distasteful to me—it didn't fit my nature at all—and I had to be constantly putting on an act, be brutal and hard, and conceal what a twirp I actually was. My glasses were constantly in the way: they gave me a piously academic appearance that wasn't suited to making me respected. That's why more and more I switched to using Anton; he was my right-hand man and accompanied me everywhere; I gave him an ample salary and his physique took care of many difficulties. I mean, like, for example, back then with Lundquist from Umeå.*

Lundquist was intelligent and for that reason unreliable. Umeå was a good market and he quickly built up a trade, employed sub-dealers on his own, and one fine day wanted to set his own purchase prices. He knew I got the goods from Narvik and informed me in a stuck-up way that he was going to go up there and get himself his own supplier.

I didn't doubt that he was going to do it and Anton and I

went up there to give him a nice reception. We ran into him down at the harbor and joined up with him. He became obviously nervous about Anton's physique and tried to bluff us, said that he'd given up the whole thing and had only gone to Narvik to find a ship—of course, it couldn't keep up forever anyway and you know where you stand with work, and so on. I said that the way things were, it wasn't easy to find a ship in Narvik and suggested that he take one of the ore boats to Antwerp, where you could find lots of ships. Lundquist looked at Anton who was smirking, and then said that maybe he'd better do that. To keep him company we offered to go over with him and buy the ticket—there was a boat sailing that very evening. In a chummy way Anton linked arms with him and I said something to the effect that of course we were going to miss him.

On the way he changed his mind and asked whether it wouldn't be better if we talked bluntly about things—he wanted to go back to Umeå and continue; after all he'd just wanted to earn a little more and surely no one could object to that. After all, we'd also like to earn as much as possible. Precisely, I replied. That's why we really feel you should go off and sail—you know where you stand with work and so on. Besides, the ocean air is good for your health and there was already a new dealer employed in Umeå. That made him totally furious and Anton had to slap him a little before he calmed down again.

It was a splendid moment when he bought the ticket to Antwerp at the office with his own money. Afterward we took him along to a cafe to get some food and we promised to go with him to the boat and wave goodbye to him. You could've died laughing looking at him standing there at the railing scowling back at us as the boat glided out of the harbor. Anton felt we should've given him a little beating first.

9

Several days later the dealer in Malmberget was arrested, but since nothing more came of it, we figured that he'd kept his trap shut. Since I was running the risk that one fine day the Narvik-connection might go down the drain, I got another import connection arranged through Östersund,* and when everything was peaceful and quiet and was going the way it was supposed to, I travelled to Stockholm to organize sales there. From the time I lived on Dannemora Street I knew an unemployed baker who was a good guy who hated regular work and was a little romantically inclined. I made him the main dealer for Stockholm; he was a good buddy and deserved that lottery prize, and I could be certain that he'd never reveal where the cigarettes came from. From there I went to Gothenburg where on the same occasion I made a connection with a stoker on the boat to Oslo; that way I was getting merchandise by three routes and could keep running the business even if something happened.

Naturally there were other people besides us who were smuggling Norwegian cigarettes into Sweden, but I don't believe on that scale and not as systematically. Incidentally, whenever the opportunity arose, I wanted to take a little closer look at that situation and find ways to manage to put a stop to that nuisance, either by informing on them or by getting their suppliers to cut them off.

10

I haven't tried to make you believe that I was a hero. And I've said to you that I can't stand heroes. I'm a person of small caliber, who, if my upbringing hadn't been so harsh that I had to run away from it, would've become a prison guard or welfare office head clerk or something like that. With my knack for making up tall tales maybe I could also have become a kind of third-rate author. If I'd had the opportunity to go to university, I'd probably have become a lawyer. You see, I don't make myself look better than I am: I'm a weak character, a little untruthful, a little unreliable, a little bit of a twirp, who's always dreamed of lying on his back on the side of the road with yellow dandelions and staring up at the clouds, and hasn't even been able to pull that off. I think it's my upbringing that's to blame for that.

If I'd had a different upbringing, presumably I could've led the smuggling operation forward into a big and flourishing business. For hours on end I've pondered why things didn't wind up going that way, why I didn't continue now that I'd gotten off the ground so well. Or in any case didn't wind it down in a reasonable way. To be perfectly blunt, I think I got scared. Not scared of the police, but scared because I was a success and the business was flourishing and was operating on a larger and larger scale. It's as if I were made for defeat and adversity—that's my element; I simply wasn't able to stand the success, which knocked the ground out from under my feet. It frightened me that the money was pouring into my pockets; I became troubled by suddenly having power over other human beings, by being able to give orders, in fact, having to give orders. The whole thing had come about so naturally and I was sitting in the middle of it when it dawned on me what had happened. In fact, I became frightened, I became nervous, couldn't sleep at night, wished that I was walking on a road in Switzerland or some other place way the hell out, just far away, a place where nobody knew me, without responsibility, without obligations, just go straight down the road, beg for a packet of food, sleep in a barn, sit and look at the sunset over the mountains.

I tried to make myself believe that the whole balloon was going to burst one day anyway. That, of course, it couldn't keep going forever. That it was smart to pull out of it in time.

Even though I knew perfectly well that that was a lie. The enterprise was solid, it could keep going for years, and I could've earned myself a fortune. A couple of arrests wouldn't have been able to destroy it—I'd covered myself in every which way.

I'd also honestly tried to stick it out, said to myself that I'd keep it going. In any case for a while. In any case until I could get out with the money I'd earned. The way things were now, the bulk of it was sunk in goods, which were lying in one place or another. Or were en route. I had to slow down the imports, sell out, and see to it that I got away.

Eighth Chapter

1

When it began to dawn on me that I wasn't born to be head of a smuggling racket, I had in mind something along the lines that I could get going on something else with the money I had. Maybe a cigar shop in Copenhagen. A cigar shop on Vesterbro Street.* Whenever I'd been in such a store, I'd always been waited on by a nice, well-dressed man, who seemed to be one of the people who had it easiest in this world. I mean, it's just not work to go over to a shelf, take a pack of cigarettes, put it on the counter, and say there you are. And besides, you're your own boss, there's no one who can order you about, no one who can say that you're permitted to do that and not permitted to do that. A nice little store like that with a good trade. Which maybe even brought in so much that I could have someone to look after it and take a walk out in Deer Park,* if I wanted to, and sit in Studenterkilden* and nurse a cup of coffee and think about back then when you were a smuggler in Sweden.

Maybe then I'd get married; then my wife could look after the store while my son and I went off to fish in Lake Bagsværd.* Then I'd sit in the boat and tell him what kind of experiences his father had had—I mean, you don't need to be ashamed of something like that once you've come out on top. Then it's just adventurous and romantic, and people say something about its being good for you to try a little of everything in life while you're young and so on. But when you're sitting in a people's kitchen telling the same story, it looks totally different—then there's no air of romance and adventure, then it just means that you've been a twirp, who hasn't been able to make it in this world.

And so of course I didn't get a wife or a cigar shop, and when I go out in Deer Park, it's to sell shoestrings to the picnickers.

2

I fled from the whole thing. Totally without any reason. One night. I'd gone down to play a game of billiards; I was supposed to meet Anton at the parlor and there was a terrible bunch of nonsense that had to be taken care of. I hadn't had a moment's rest the last few months—there was always a row, if not about this, then about that. I'd dreamed about going to Abisko* to ski and hobnob with the upper crust, but it was clear that there could never be time for that. Not for a moment was I able to turn my back on my organization—I was chained to it. Day and night. And there'd never be an end to it. Not until sometime maybe when they put me in the penitentiary.

And now I was going to go down and play billiards and listen to their nonsense. And they expected me to make decisions and have a big mouth. And I was a born petty-bourgeois and wasn't going to be able to keep it up in the long run. It'd be wonderful to say goodbye to all of that, cast off the yoke of slavery. And as I was standing outside the cafe, the thought came to me that in fact I could just as well do it this evening as any other time.

3

I took the train directly to Copenhagen. I arrived on the train-ferry at the main railway station early one morning and sat down in the restaurant to have coffee and have a look in the newspapers for cigar shops for sale. When the waiter brought the coffee, he turned out to be one of my schoolmates, named Jeppe, a ruddy-cheeked, yellow-haired fellow, who was always kicking me in the shin in order to get me to bawl. Things weren't going well, he said; his father had had a cigar shop on Vesterbro Street, a dog's life, old boy, tied up from morning till evening, no profit, had to close, the times, you understand, the crisis. He kept standing and chit-chatting, till an old lady, who had a little hawk's nose and resembled a turkey, had screamed *waiter* eight times. Before he went over to her, he kicked me in the shin for old times' sake.

I went right to a travel agency and bought a ticket to Paris. I mean, you have be some place in the world and one's as good as the next.

4

And that's the way it continued; I hardly know whether I care to tell any more and whether you care to hear any more. I mean, my life was just a perpetual repetition of itself. It was the same thing and the same thing and the same thing. Nonstop. A treadmill. I had a sense of being cheated out of life's real experiences; my existence was worthless. And I'd never ever wind up experiencing what was really of value. The whole thing had been a mess and a failure from the start. No matter what I got involved in, nothing ever came of it—not even as a criminal was I able to make it—all I could do was shuffle around in life and pull off little scams.

I blew all my money in Paris and went to the Riviera, to Nice, where I supported myself as a kind of tour guide. If you're going to be able to live on that, you can't be too moral. And I lived on it. But not especially well. And when one day I heard a new consul had arrived in Marseille, I went over and got sent back to Denmark through Berlin. In Berlin for a half a year I was at a private detective agency that specialized in destroying marriages and otherwise got its revenues from blackmail. During that half-year I experienced plenty of what's called material, material for a novel—you see, we procured grounds for divorce. If we weren't able to manage to compromise a man one way, there was always another way that proved successful. If the wife wanted to get divorced and would give a reasonable part of her alimony, we'd certainly arrange things. In a pinch she'd fire her maid and hire a lady we had especially for that. The new maid was out to hook the man of the house and as a rule it's not hard for a shapely girl to seduce a man. When it was time and the moment had been chosen, the wife unexpectedly came home with a friend and barged into the bedroom, where her tangible grounds for divorce were taking place in bed. Naturally there were husbands who wouldn't walk into the trap; in such cases the girl would lure the poor man under some pretext or other into the bedroom, lock the door and fling the key out the window, take off her dress, rip her underclothes, knock over a couple of chairs, and scream for help, whereupon the wife and the friend, who'd coincidentally come home at that very moment, would open the door with the help of another key and free the poor girl. When the matter came before the court, both the judge and the audience smirked when the husband explained that it was the girl herself who'd taken off her clothes and ripped her chemise. Then, when the wife had won the case and gotten judgment for her alimony, our actual work began by getting her, on every possible pretext, to hand over one sum bigger than the next. Naturally, we didn't threaten her directly with letting everything come to light; we had more effective and less risky methods. Maybe it was the actress we'd engaged to rip her underwear who'd go to the police and confess everything if we didn't help her with a ticket to South America; maybe it was a detective who'd been fired who'd keep his mouth shut only if we bought him a cafe in Wedding.* In any event, we'd of course be terribly sorry about a possible scandal, but we ourselves didn't have at our disposal the whole amount necessary and were hoping for understanding and support.

The head of the agency was named Haubitz and had formerly been a private detective for a Hohenzollern prince. In any case, that's what was printed on the firm's card, and I've never waded in so much smut as during that half-year. It ended up with my intimidating him into giving me money to travel to Paris.

5

In a way, a new chapter of my life began with that trip. As

I stood at Gare du Nord,* all my spirits had abandoned me; it was as if my life were finished, had come to a standstill, and couldn't start up again. According to the plan, now I was just going to see about getting some money to pay for a hotel room and a little food and otherwise let tomorrow take care of tomorrow. And the day after I was going to do the same, and sooner or later an opportunity would turn up, which it was merely a matter of seizing. I'd been in that situation hundreds of times before and virtually had a whole system to go by. It was routine work pure and simple.

But as I was standing there at Gare du Nord and was on the verge of getting started on conquering a kind of existence for myself, I suddenly came to a standstill. I couldn't go on. I put my suitcase in the checkroom and went for a walk through the streets in order to get this little fit of insanity over with.

And I wandered all day and all night up and down the streets, and the more I tried to come to my senses, the worse it became. I was hungry and tried not even to think about how I could get some food. I was dead tired and could probably have found a way to get into a bed, but it was as if I was too tired of this constant struggle to be able to concern myself with that question. The skin between my toes was raw from my having trudged on the cobblestones, my socks were chafing my skin and hurt, my ankles were swollen, and I couldn't even decide to go into a park and sit down on a bench.

And that little fit of insanity still wouldn't let go of me, and when I began pondering how it had come about, it occurred to me that at the train station I'd seen a poster with my birth date and that's how it occurred to me that in a few days I'd be thirty years old. And that was the ridiculous thought that had knocked the sense out of me and wouldn't leave me alone.*

Because that meant that if my life wasn't going to crumble away like sand through my fingers, I'd have to take stock of my existence and draw up a budget for the remaining half of my life. If in fact it wasn't too late.

And that's why it didn't matter whether I got to bed and whether I got food and whether a woman gave me the glad eye and whether I was in Paris or any other place.

And the thought about saving my life before it was too late still wouldn't let go of me and not till the sun rose did I fling myself on the bank of the Seine and fall asleep.

And when I woke up, the thought was still there and I was just as afraid of the future as a condemned man.

6

If a person's going to tell about his life, he's inclined to tell about the purely external experiences he's had: then he was in an apprenticeship, he says, then he became a soldier and then he was in Magasin du Nord* for five years and then he broke his leg and then he won a prize for bowling some way or other and got into the newspaper with the ball and prize and looked serious and determined in the picture and then he got married and became a warehouse manager and since then actually nothing's happened that's worth telling about.

Just as world history is just lists of kings and wars. Maybe people should tell their story in a different way: the external experiences don't mean all that damn much—I've had plenty of them and my existence has been aimless and dull. But maybe it would be hard to tell about what's happening inside yourself; I mean, it's there and working inside you, you can't check up on it, but all of a sudden one day the upheaval is accomplished, it breaks out, and overturns everything.

7

Human beings presumably have an ideal they're trying ultimately to resemble; when all of a sudden one morning they behave in a different way than usually, maybe that's because they've changed ideals. Some have maybe a whole set of ideals to switch to. Naturally, it's not true of personalities, but incidentally who is a personality. In any case, I'm not and I've never met any.

A human being has only one life and the fear of being cheated out of what really was of value here in life made me switch ideals. I wanted to be respectable and industrious, I wanted to have a home, wife, and child. I wanted to forget ditches by the side of the road and all that nonsense about freedom, forget that I hated to knuckle under and take orders; I'd be free to live together with other people I liked and who liked me. I never attained freedom, after all, and even if I attained it, I was so constituted that I wasn't able to live in it; I was raised to obedience, and even though I'd rebelled and fled, my upbringing had warped me to such a degree that I wasn't able to act independently.

8

Everyone else did their job and lived in a normal and sensible way, sat at home in the evening and listened to the radio, read the weeklies, and played with their children. And when they came home in the evening their kids shouted in the entrance hall: *Daddy's coming*, and when they went into the living room, their wife was standing there with a calm, warm smile that said: *I've missed you so much*.

And I was lying there by the Seine dreaming about living like other people and feeling two soft arms around my neck. Not a whore's arms, not a ticket girl at the movies I seduced, but a wife's arms. Up on the bridge the busses raced off with people who conformed and lived normally and on the river barges glided past with family life and geraniums in the stern and the unemployed who were standing on the bank fishing went home for dinner to their wives with what they'd caught.

9

I got a job as a cloakroom attendant at the Danish cafe on

*rue Servandoni** and I had a modest room at a little hotel near *Place Nation* and I tried to make the room resemble a home. And I tried to stay at home in my free time, bought a house jacket, a smoker's table, and a little radio. At work I was serious and polite and I didn't use any more money than was absolutely necessary.

But when I sat in my room, I had to make a violent effort to keep sitting in the chair with my book. On the way home on the bus I always used to say to myself: Well, old boy, tonight we'll have a really comfy time; I forced myself to whistle and when I got up to the room, I pottered about for a long time, changed jackets, changed shoes, tidied up, and turned on the radio—all of it to create the atmosphere that makes a room into a home. I'd bought a pipe and despite the fact that I liked smoking cigarettes better, I filled my pipe, leaned back in the chair, and forced myself to say: Ah, you're having a comfy time after all, a pipe full of tobacco and a good book.

And I thought it was probably a matter of habit and what pleasure was there actually in tearing up and down the streets. And I got up and went over to the window and hundreds of times I was about to take my hat and leave, but I forced myself to sit down again and keep reading. And I thought that it was that stuff with the wife and all that stuff that was missing.

10

And all over the earth that's the way human beings lived—they had a little hole in the wall, a woman, kids, and they had a job. And when they died, there was somebody who cried, somebody who put flowers on their grave, and missed them. And if I died, nobody would miss me and it'd hardly be noticed.

Then I got to know Jeanine and life began to take shape. Jeanine waited tables at an eatery on *rue Vavin* and had a body like a French photograph and a face like an angel.

Ninth Chapter

1

We took a walk in the Bois de Boulogne* and Jeanine was a perfectly ordinary girl who wanted to get married and didn't believe I was serious about it. And she had an uncle who could get me a job in a mansion as a doorman and we'd have it so good.

And I came to love everything that was ordinary and we did everything that ordinary people do. We made excursions and visited her family and bought cheap little things for the home that would become a reality as soon as I could start the job. And one day she brought a pair of embroidered slippers for me and one day I bought a porcelain teapot and six cups and saucers. And she sewed buttons on my shirts and made me happy by saying that I should take care of my clothes. And at a photographer's on Boulevard Montparnasse there was a display case with photographs of little children, which we always had to stop and look at, and so I'd be a doorman the rest of my life and Jeanine would earn a little extra by helping out at the master and mistress's.

And then one morning Jeanine came into the Danish cafe on *rue Servandoni* while I was doing some polishing and said that she'd gotten word that I could start work in three weeks. And she had on a flowery dress made of thin material and she resembled a picture in *La vie parisienne*,* but her face was like a child's, and now I was finally about to live like other people and be happy.

And two weeks before the wedding I got drunk because I knew that I wouldn't be in a position to go through with it, because I wasn't going to be able to be a doorman the rest of my days.

And a week before the wedding I wrote a letter to Jeanine and begged her forgiveness and two days later I was in Copenhagen.

— — —

And several days later I went to Sweden and in order to earn a little on the way I took along thirty packs of *Flag*,* which I was going to sell in Malmö, and as I was going to sell the first one, I was arrested and put in jail and after three weeks I was sentenced to pay the Swedish state damages and was deported from the Kingdom of Sweden for all time.*

And when I was standing in Copenhagen again, I didn't have any money to buy food with and went up to a house to beg. The first place there was nobody home and a lower-level railwayman, or else he was a lieutenant—in any event something like that—lived at the second place and he called the police and I was convicted of begging.

— — —

And since then everything I've touched has gone wrong for me: if I try to do a little deal, I'm arrested, if I sleep in a railway car, I can be certain there'll be a raid that very night—my luck has abandoned me.

I've often thought about the fact that it'd actually be easier to put an end to it all, take a little gas or something like that, but I've never been able to make up my mind to do it, not because I'm a coward, but I've quite simply not felt like it.

And up till a couple of days ago I was living in a rusted-out car—it was my home and that's the way I felt about it. And I wanted to do so much and had such big plans about freedom and so on, and then it ends up with me living in a rusted-out car and I'm happy about it.

But actually I'm not dissatisfied with life and sometimes I'm comfortable with the feeling that I've tricked the people who wanted to trick me. You see, my triumph is that I didn't become a parish deacon or something like that—I was brought up to do that and I tricked them. I tricked the whole lot of them. You're brought up to be nice and well-behaved, to toil and slave for other people without getting anything for it, and to die just as poor as when you were born. And when folks become discontented with having to slave away night and day and still be poor as a church mouse, people console them by saying that salt and bread make your cheeks red* and telling them the story of the world's happiest man, who didn't even own a shirt. But they haven't been able to pull that one on me; I've tricked the whole bunch of them—my father and my mother, my aunts, the teachers, the newspapers and the church, the pastor and the whole education system, the whole society—there they were having trouble with me, thrashing me and preaching and ordering and trying to manage to make a gardener or doorman or custodian or something else solid out of me—and then the whole thing was a waste, I tricked them totally and completely; the whole system's been wasted on me.

They made up the story of the happiest man without a shirt so people wouldn't feel discontented in their slavery. They couldn't pull that one on me and I'm proud of it. So the lamb won't make a fuss about being shorn, they say that God tempers the wind to it.

— — —

Unfortunately I don't have my rusted-out car any more: a few days ago there was somebody in it when I got home and I had my glasses smashed and had to walk the streets at night.

Notes

The bolded numbers at the left refer to the pages of *God Tempers the Wind to the Shorn Lamb* on which the italicized text appears.

1 *But one day . . .*:This entire italicized passage bears a resemblance to the parable of the laborers in the vineyard in Matthew 20:1-16 and Luke 20:9-18, but it is not taken directly from the Bible. In his recent thesis submitted to Copenhagen University, Jacob Wraae Nielsen interprets the passage as a pastiche of constructed biblical tidings designed as an ironic commentary on the role of the Christian church and morality in instilling conformity. Jacob Wraae Nielsen, "Mogens Klitgaards livssyn—en læsning af tre romaner og en novelle med afsæt i eksistentialistisk teori" 59-60 (Specialeopgave, Institut for Nordisk Filologi, Copenhagen University, Oct. 2001). To be sure, the saying "God tempers the wind to the shorn lamb" is not biblical. In English it is most often associated with Laurence Sterne's use of it: "She had since that, she told me, strayed as far as Rome, and walked round St Peter's once—and returned back—that she had found her way alone across the Apennines—had travelled over all Lombardy without money—and through the flinty roads of Savoy without shoes—how she had borne it, and how she had got supported, she could not tell—*but God tempers the wind*, said Maria, to the shorn lamb." Laurence Sterne, *A Sentimental Journey Through France and Italy* 139 (Graham Petrie ed.; Harmondsworth: Penguin, 1982 [1768]). It can nevertheless be traced back at least to the Frenchman Henri Estienne, who used it in 1594: "Dieu mesure le froid à la brébis tondue." *The Home Book of Quotations: Classical and Modern* 789 (Burton Stevenson ed.; 10th ed.; New York: Dodd, Mead, 1967 [1934]). That the saying appears to have more currency in Denmark than in the United States may be related to the fact that the painter Rasmus Larsen used it as the title of one of the ornamental friezes he painted in the lobby of the Danish parliament. See above "A Note on the Cover," p. xxiv.

3 *parish deacon*: A *kordegn* (literally "choir deacon"), which lacks an equivalent in the United States, is the right-hand of and administrative assistant to the pastor in the Danish Lutheran church, performing certain functions during the service itself such as reading the opening and closing prayer. However, in Denmark, where various civil registrations are associated with the church, the *kordegn* also takes care of registering births, deaths, and namings, in addition to keeping the church's accounts. Email from Edel Steffensen, acting *kordegn*, Haraldskirken, Høje Gladsaxe (Dec. 13, 2001); email from Vivi Jensen, *kordegn*, Thomas Kingo Kirke, Odense (Dec. 14, 2001). Every Lutheran church in Denmark has a *kordegn* and all Danes are intimately familiar with the position.

4 *Frederiksholm*: In the 1920s the Copenhagen city dump was located in the southwestern corner of the city. Harald Eriksen, "Hammelstrupsvej," in *Sydvest Folkeblad* (updated Apr. 23, 2001), on http://www.sv-folkeblad.dk/lokalhistorie/lokalhistorie199701.html# LOKALHISTORIE.

4 *Coastal Road*: Strandvejen, which runs from Copenhagen north along the Sound, was the location of many huge villas owned by nouveaux-riches World War I profiteers.

4 *Larsbjørn Lane*: Larsbjørnstræde is located in downtown Copenhagen near City Hall.

4 *the people's kitchen*: Unlike a soup kitchen, a *folkekøkken* is not free; run or subsidized by local governments, it provides cheap meals to the poor. People's kitchens were first established in Copenhagen in March 1917 under the impact of wartime inflation and fuel shortages, which caused the municipal authorities to impose severe restrictions on the population's use of cooking gas. Although at first they served only dinner, later they offered comprehensive meal service. N. Andreasen et al., "Københavns Kommunes Administration," in *Danmark Land og Folk: Historisk-topograifsk-statistisk Haandbog* 4: 44-69 at 50 (separately paginated) (Daniel Bruun ed.; Copenhagen: Gyldendalske Boghandel, 1922); Sigurd Jensen, *Under fælles ansvar* 166-67, in *Københavns historie*, vol. 5: *1900-45* (Sv. Cedergreen Bech et al. eds.; Copenhagen: Gyldendal, 1981). Klitgaard himself frequented Copenhagen's people's kitchens when he was down and out. Poul Carit Andersen, "Mogens Klitgaard," in Mogens Klitgaard, *de sindssyges klode* 5-28 at 11 (Copenhagen: Carit Andersen, 1968).

5 *Humlebæk*: A coastal town north of Copenhagen about 3 miles south of Elsinore.

5 *Halland*: A region of Sweden along the Kattegat north of the Danish island of Zealand.

6 *Ängelholm*: A Swedish coastal town about 17 miles from Hälsingborg, which is located directly across the Sound from Elsinore.

6 *crown*: The *krona* is the Swedish currency.

6 *lodgings for travellers*: Klitgaard uses in italics the Swedish *rum för resande*.

6 *I came to a crowd of day laborers; most of them were Poles*: Many thousands of (especially female and child) seasonal farmworkers migrated from Poland, where small plots and lagging industrialization generated agrarian unemployment and underemployment, to Germany, Denmark and (to a lesser degree) Sweden in the late nineteenth and early twentieth century to cultivate and harvest sugar beets. Zdzislaw Ludkiewicz, "The Agrarian Structure of Poland and France from the Point of View of Emigration," *International Labour Review* 22:155-76 at 163 (1930). Polish farmworkers' seasonal migration to Germany began about 1870. G. Rabinovitch, "The Seasonal Emigration of Agricultural Workers to Germany," *International Labour Review* 25:213-35, 332-67 (1932). Danish sugar beet factories, which began operating in 1874, recruited Swedish girls to work in the fields; this migration stopped about 1906 when Swedish farms were able to employ the unemployed farmworkers from southern Sweden. Polish workers migrated to Denmark between 1893 and 1929, when the increased unemployment associated with the Depression caused Danish men to begin performing this work. The number of Polish workers in Denmark peaked at 12,452 in 1914, dropping sharply and permanently thereafter. Georg Nellemann, *Polske landarbejdere i Danmark og deres efterkommere: Et studie af landarbejder-invandringen 1893-1929 og invandrernes integration i det danske samfund i to generationer* 20-54, 120 (Copenhagen: Nationalmuseet, 1981); Jens Warming, *Danmarks erhvervs- og samfundsliv: En lærebog i Danmarks statistik* 59 (Copenhagen: Gad, 1930); Euzebiusz Basiński, "Poles Abroad," in *Poland: A Handbook* 146-73 at 154 (Warsaw: Interpress, 1977). The harsh conditions of the Polish workers' employment, which included contracts that they were not permitted to terminate, led to regulatory legislation in 1908 establishing police supervision of contractual relations. Lov vedrørende Anvendelse af udenlandske Arbejdere til Arbejde i visse Virksomheder samt det offentliges Tilsyn dermed, Law No. 229 of Aug. 21, 1908, in *Lovtidende for 1908*, at 903-909; Nellemann, *Polske landarbejdere i Danmark* at 73-85. Between 1904 and 1914, about a thousand Polish (and Galician) farm laborers were recruited annually to work on sugar-beet farms in southern Sweden, where emigration (in large part to the United States) and industrialization had led to a labor shortage, at least under the inferior conditions offered by the farm owners. As in Denmark, some Polish laborers remained in Sweden after World War I began; though some left during the 1920s, others settled in Sweden. Tomas Hammar, "Sverige åt svenskarna: Invandringspolitik, utlänningskontroll och asylrätt 1900-1932," at 32-34, 49, 397 (Doctoral dissertation; Stockholm: Stockholm University, 1964). According to "Labour Problems in Sugar-Beet Production in Denmark, Germany, and Sweden," *International Labour Review* 21:244-54 at 249-50 (1930), no agricultural laborers entered Sweden after World War I.

6 *luffare*: Swedish for tramp or vagabond.

7 *farmstead*: *Avlsgård* was that part of a landed estate where the actual farming took place.

7 *a Copenhagen basement wash house*: A bare room with a cement floor, a large vat, and a huge pot for boiling the clothes.

11 *the high-heel slippers changed her, made her instep slimmer and her calf rounder*: On the physiology and ideology of these effects, see Marc Linder, "Smart Women, Stupid Shoes, and Cynical Employers: The Unlawfulness and Adverse Health Consequences of Sexually Discriminatory Workplace Footwear Requirements for Female Employees," *Journal of Corporation Law* 22:295-329 (1997); Marc Linder and Charles Saltzman, "A History of Medical Scientists on High Heels," *International Journal of Health Services* 28:201-25 (1998).

14 *registered*: The farm had to register him with the police.

15 *parish church council*: After a half-century's existence on a voluntary basis, the *Menighedsråd* became statutorily mandatory in all parishes in Denmark beginning in 1904. In addition to the parish minister, who was chairman, it consisted of at least four representatives—all men and women at least twenty-five years old were eligible—elected by the congregation for six- (and, after 1912, four-) year terms. It had to meet at least four times annually, and it had to be consulted with regard to all questions decisively affecting the congregation's religious life. It also gained control over the church's collections for the poor. Harald Jørgensen, *Lokaladministrationen i Danmark: Oprindelse og historisk udvikling indtil 1970*, at 379-81 (Copenhagen: Gad, 1985).

19 *Halmstad*: A Swedish coastal town on the Kattegat about 70 miles north of Copenhagen; it was Sweden's nineteenth largest city in

1925 with a population of 18,381. Kungl. Statistisk Centralbyrån, *Årsbok för Sverige 1926*, tab. 10 at 8 (Stockholm: Norstedt, 1926).

19 *Falkenberg*: A Swedish coastal town 25 miles north of Halmstad.

19 *beachcomber*: The Danish word *betskummer* (or *bitskummer*), which derives from the English "beachcomber," can also mean a man without permanent employment who hangs out in ports and cadges from the sailors docking there. *Ordbog over det danske Sprog* Supp. Vol. 2:92 (Copenhagen: Gyldendal, 1995).

20 *police*: Klitgaard uses the Swedish word with the Danish plural definite suffix *poliserne.*

20 *the luffer were freed from reporting their arrival and departure*: In Sweden and Denmark and other European countries, people who move from one city to another are required to register with the national residence registration office (*folkeregister*), whereas those such as vagabonds who had no permanent address registered with the police. Because municipalities feared being stuck with liability for paying poor relief to vagabonds, they sought to remove them to the municipalities from which they came and which had the legal responsibility for maintaining them.

20 *spikes*: Klitgaard uses the Swedish *spik*, which is recognizable to Danes as the Danish *spiger* with the same meaning.

20 *Norrland*: Sweden's northern division with a population of 1,018,009 and a population density of only 4 inhabitants per square kilometer at the 1920 census, Norrland was the country's smallest demographically. *The Encyclopædia Britannica: The New Volumes* 32:629 (12th ed.; London: Encyclopædia Britannica, 1922).

21 *hawkers:* Klitgaard uses the Swedish word (with a Danish plural ending) *nasarne*, which is not comprehensible to Danes.

21 *honest social ambitions*: An ironic phrase from two comedies by Ludvig Holberg (1684-1754), the leading figure of the Danish enlightenment. In one, a character seeks to distinguish his honest ambition from rage for rank. Ludvig Holberg, *Den honnette Ambition*, in *Holberg Comoedierne* 3:101-39 at 107 (Carl Roos ed.; Copenhagen: Aschehoug, 1924 [1741]). In the other, a character states that what among men is called rage for rank, is called honest ambition among women. Ludvig Holberg, *Philosophus udi egen Indbildning*, in *Holberg Comoedierne* 3:321-81 at 376-77 (1754).

21 *small communities*: Klitgaard uses a pseudo-Danish spelling (*samhæller*) of the Swedish word *samhällen*.

21 *a dollar*: A *daler* was until 1873 a Danish coin worth two crowns. Derived from the German *Taler*, the word was used in all the Scandinavian languages.

21 *Värmlands-Kalle*: Värmland is a county in west-central Sweden; Kalle is the equivalent of Charlie.

23 *I ingratiated myself with him*: The phrase *Jeg brændte på ham* could also mean: "I gave him a light."

23 *Thurø*: A small island off the southeast coast of the larger island of Funen near the town of Svendborg.

25 *ordinary seamen*: An ordinary seaman is a member of the deck department and subordinate to an able seaman; he has learned part of the trade and performs general maintenance and repair work. After passing an examination, he is eligible to become an able seaman. René de Kerchove, *International Maritime Dictionary* 554 (2d ed.; New York: Van Nostrand, 1961).

25 *a discharge book*: An 1861 law required every Danish sailor to have in his possession a *søfartsbog* with information about when and where he had signed on and been discharged, his liability for military service, and other matters. *Ordbog over det danske sprog* 23:273 (5th ed.; Copenhagen: Gyldendal, 1996 [1946]). U.S. law since 1936 has called for a "continuous discharge book." 46 U.S. Code sect. 7202 (2001) (codifying Act of June 25, 1936, ch. 816, sect. 3, 49 Stat. 1930).

26 *skerries*: The *Oxford English Dictionary*'s definition ("A rugged insulated sea-rock or stretch of rocks covered by the sea at high water or in stormy weather; a reef") does not adequately describe this unique Swedish phenomenon, which includes islands with grass and woods and bare cliffs shooting up out of the seas; although the *skärgård* off Stockholm are the best known, off Sweden's west coast from Gothenburg northward lies an archipelago or belt of skerries, islands and cliffs extending four to eight miles seaward and making navigation intricate. *Oxford English Dictionary* 15:593 (2d ed.; Oxford: Clarendon Press, 1989); National Imagery and Mapping Agency, *Sailing Direction (Enroute): Skagerrak and Kattegat* 83 (8th ed.; Bethesda, 2000).

26 *Fruit soup*: *Sødsuppe* is made with fruit syrup, prunes, raisins, and sago.

28 *ØK*: The Østasiastiske Kompagni (East Asiatic Company) was a large Danish colonial trading and shipping firm.

28 *Skagen*: A town located at the extreme northern tip of Jutland where the Skagerrak and Kattegat, two arms of the North Sea, meet.

28 *close-hauled*: "The trim of a vessel's sails when it endeavors to make progress in the nearest direction possible toward that point of the compass from which the wind blows." de Kerchove, *International Maritime Dictionary* at 154.

29 *ox-hide shoes*: This type of shoe, which "recalls shoes from 'stone age,'" was commonly worn in the villages in the Faeroe Islands until World War II. It was made of ox-hide (or horse-hide or sealskin), from which the hair had been removed and which was then tanned in tormentil. The shoes were sewn with a seam in the middle in the back and front; two shoestrings were drawn through two holes in the front and two in the back, wound a couple of times around the ankle, and the ends were inserted under the laces in front. Klitgaard does not say what the shoes were made of (and probably did not know), calling them merely *skindsko*; since "leather shoes" would be misleading and "hide shoes" is not a term in use in English, it is assumed that the shoes were ox-hide. Similar shoes made of sheepskin were generally worn by women and children, who often wore those shoes underneath wooden shoes. Email from Regin Debess, National Museum of the Faroe Islands (Feb. 20 and 21, 2002). The stronger ox-hide shoes were, according to Tóri í Hoyvík, the city gardener of Tórshavn, "slippery to wear, but everybody used it in the villages maybe 70 years ago when in the mountains gathering sheep or in the cliffs catching birds (there they put a woollen outer shoe on to prevent sliding in the birds' guano) as well as on the sea fishing." Email from Tóri í Hoyvík (Feb. 21, 2002).

29 *Thorshavn*: The capital of the Faroe Islands.

29 *roads*: A less enclosed place than a harbor, where ships can safely lie at anchor. See, e.g., Hampton Roads, Virginia.

29 *Selletræ*: The Danish spelling of the small Faroese village of Selatrad, which is located about 45 miles from Thorshavn.

31 *Grimsby*: A port on the east coast near Hull.

31 *The Orkney Islands*: They are located north of Scotland at about the same latitude as the southern tip of Norway.

31 *lay to*: A ship lies to when the wind and sea conditions prevent it from continuing on its course.

31 *Langelinie pier*: A very popular place to promenade in Copenhagen.

35 *Hovedstaden*: *The Capital* was a newspaper published from Nov. 26, 1912 until Mar. 9, 1920, when it was absorbed into *Kristeligt Dagblad*. The founders of the paper wished to "combat the modern press's immorality and—in a struggle against Politiken—support the people's regeneration on a religious and national basis." Jette Søllinge and Niels Thomsen, *De danske aviser 1634-1989,* 2:216 (Odense: Odense universitetsforlag, [1988]-1991).

35 *Kristeligt Dagblad*: *Christian Daily* was from its founding in 1896 associated with the Church Association for the Inner Mission, a puritanical, pietistic, revivalist movement within the Lutheran Church. Søllinge and Thomsen, *De danske aviser 1634-1989,* 2:195-96.

36 *bear skin fescue*: *Festuca scoparia* is neat football-like rounded clumps of green foliage producing flower-heads in June and July.

37 *The United's*: Det Forenede Dampskibs-Selskab (The United Steamship Company), which was founded in 1866 by the financier C. F. Tietgen, gained a quasi-monopoly over Danish shipping.

37 *butter boat*: Danish butter exports to England were the country's biggest export item and as such the linchpin of the import-dependent Danish economy.

37 *"Primula"*: "Primrose."

37 *Little Parrot Street*: There once was a Kleine Papageienstraße in Altona. http://www.fulgura.de/1800/md42-inx.htm.

37 *Altona*: At the end of the eighteenth century Altona, located on the Elbe River directly west of Hamburg, into which it was incorporated in 1937, was the second largest city in Denmark.

42 *German South Jutlander*: A *sønderjyde* is an inhabitant of South Jutland/North Schleswig. After World War I this area was returned to Denmark after having been part of Germany since the war of 1864.

44 *it was right after the vote in South Jutland*: In accordance with the Treaty of Versailles, with a 91.5 percent participation rate, three-fourths of the voters of so-called Zone 1 (the southern border of which ran north of Flensburg) voted on February 10, 1920 to be reunited with Denmark, while one-fourth voted to remain part of Germany. Erik Rasmussen, *Velfærdsstaten på vejen: 1913-1939*, at 210-18, in *Danmarks historie*, vol. 14 (John Danstrup and Hal Koch eds.; Copenhagen: Politiken, 1965).

45 *sex appeal*: Klitgaard uses the phrase in English.

47 *grebes*: A type of swimming and diving bird.

50 *main train station*: That is, in Copenhagen.

51 *Valby-Povl*: Valby is a section of Copenhagen; Klitgaard was born there.

51 *Kruså*: A small border town directly north of Flensburg.

52 *Why not get sent home*: A *hjemsender* is an indigent Dane sent back to his home parish within Denmark or repatriated by a Danish consulate abroad to Denmark. *Ordbog over det danske Sprog* 8:234 (5th ed.; Copenhagen: Gyldendal 1994 [1926]).

52 *Angleterre*: The Hotel d'Angleterre was Copenhagen's fanciest and best-known hotel.

53 *Brœddehytten*: Wooden Cottage was and is a famous restaurant in the amusement park Bakken in Deer Park outside Copenhagen.

53 *Gedser*: Located on the island of Falster, it is the southernmost Danish town, where ferries carrying rail passengers to and from Rostock, Germany depart and land.

54 *Wivel*: A famous restaurant in Copenhagen, which was later renamed Wivex and from which dance music was transmitted on radio. The restaurant was owned by Carl Wivel (1844 - 1922).

54 *Lake Fure*: Furesø, Denmark's deepest lake, is located 10 miles northwest of Copenhagen.

54 *Lake Garda*: It is located in northern Italy between Brescia and Verona.

55 *Esbjerg*: Located in southern Jutland near the German border, it is Denmark's biggest west coast port and the center of the export trade to Britain. It was Denmark's seventh biggest city, with a population of 24,063, in 1925. Danmarks Statistik, *Statistisk Aarbog 1926*, tab. 6 at 9 (Copenhagen: Thiele, 1926).

55 *had a couple of German thousand mark bills on me, but they weren't worth anything—no one wanted to exchange them*: By the latter part of 1923 the dollar was worth more than a trillion marks.

55 *coal trimmer*: A trimmer (or stower) shifted the coal from storage to the stokers and made sure the coal was evenly distributed on the ship.

57 *a wholesale merchant*: Wholesale merchants were the quintessential wealthy occupational group in Denmark, the counterparts to corporation or bank presidents in the United States. See Mogens Klitgaard, *There's a Man Sitting on a Trolley* 178-79 (note to p. 2) (Marc Linder tr.; Iowa City: Fănpìhuà Press, 2001).

59 *Sir Basil Zaharoff, the armaments prince*: Zaharoff (1849-1936) was an armaments dealer who made a fortune, especially during World War I.

59 *Odense*: The principal town of the island of Funen, it was Denmark's third largest city with a population of 49,469 in 1921 and 52,208 in 1925. Danmarks Statistik, *Statistisk Aarbog 1926*, tab. 6 at 6-9.

59 *breeches buoy*: A life-saving device consisting of a canvas seat with breeches as the legs, it is hung from a life buoy suspended by rope between ships or between a ship and land.

59 *Svendborg*: A town on the southeastern coast of Funen adjacent to Thurø. Bertolt Brecht lived there as a refugee from 1933 to 1939.

62 *Fruens Bøge*: A wooded area on Odense Creek on the southern outskirts of Odense.

62 *Munkemose*: Munk's Marsh is a large park on Odense Creek near downtown Odense.

62 *Thrige*: A large Danish firm producing electrical motors. Thomas B. Thrige began his own enterprise in Odense in 1894 after returning from the United States where he had worked at the Thomas Edison laboratory. Thrige became one of the largest employers in Odense. http://thrige-titan.dk.

63 *we'll be sent to serve a prison sentence for nonpayment of child support for an illegitimate child*: Schmidt does not mean that they had actually fathered illegitimate children, but that the authorities would use vagabonds' reputation for loose relations with various women as a pretext for incarcerating them.

63 *Middelfart*: A town on the extreme western coast of Funen adjacent to Jutland with a population of 6,870 in 1921 and 7,087 in 1925. Danmarks Statistik, *Statistisk Aarbog 1926*, tab. 6 at 7.

63 *Enslev*: There are several towns by that name in Jutland, but none on Funen. *Geodætisk Instituts kort: Danmark i 1:200 000* (13th ed.; Copenhagen: Geodætisk Institut, 1955). No such place is listed in the 1921 population census. Danmarks Statistik, *Folkemængden i Februar 1921 i Kongeriget Danmark* (Copenhagen: Bianco Luno, 1921). There is a village named Indslev (sometimes also spelled Ingslev) on the road from Odense that did have an inn in the 1920s and was located about seven miles from Middelfart. See the map of Funen appended to *Danmark: Land og folk: Historisk - topografisk - statistisk Haandbog*, vol. 4 (Daniel Bruun ed.; Copenhagen: Gyldendal, 1922). It would be unusual for Klitgaard to invent a place name.

64 *pollarded*: To pollard is to cut back to the trunk to promote growth of a dense head of foliage.

64 *A ladybug was sitting on my hand and I let it fly up to Our Lord and ask for good weather tomorrow, because . . . you just do it—you learned it as a child*: Known by all Danes, this verse is perhaps the first nursery rhyme children learn. One points to the sky with the finger the ladybug is crawling on and recites the rhyme; if the ladybug does not fly off on its own, one helps it on its way by blowing on it.

65 *The King*: Christian X was the Danish king in the 1920s.

65 *the House of Oldenburg*: The Oldenburgers were the royal house from which the Danish kings descended beginning with Christian I (Count Christian of Oldenburg, who reigned from 1448 to 1481) and ending with Frederik VII (who reigned from 1848 to 1863). Oldenburg is a former Grand Duchy.

68 *the ferry*: It sailed to Jutland, probably to the town of Fredericia.

69 *pale, light beer*: *Hvidtøl* is a top-fermented, strongly malted, low-alcohol content Danish beer.

69 *a real pilsner fit for a human being*: Pilsner is virtually synonymous with beer in Denmark.

70 *Vendsyssel*: The northeasternmost part of Jutland, separated from the rest of the peninsula by the Limfjord. "Syssel" is a district.

70 *the Inner Mission*: The Church Association for the Inner Mission in Denmark, a puritanical, pietistic, revivalist movement within Danish Lutheranism, was founded in 1861. Calling themselves "de hellige" ("the Pious," "the Holy," or "the Saintly"), adherents stressed confession, repentance, conversion, and salvation, and rigidly proscribed amusements such as dancing, card playing, and alcohol. See Marc Linder, "Introduction," in Hans Kirk, *The Fishermen* xii-xiii (2d ed.; Iowa City: Fănpìhuà Press, 2000 [1999]).

71 *Gothenburg*: Sweden's second largest city is located on the Kattegat at about the same latitude as the northernmost tip of Jutland. Its population in 1925 was 231,007. Kungl. Statistisk Centralbyrån, *Årsbok för Sverige 1926*, tab. 10 at 8.

71 *Danish printers . . . had a fine benefits system, travelled by train from town to town and travelled around like other tourists*: Among printers, as with other trade unions whose roots went back to the old gilds, there was a custom that, when they came to a town abroad, they could go to the local trade union and get shelter and a "donation," which at that time was a fixed sum (travel money), which made it possible to make ends meet until they got to the next town if there was no work in the first town. The local union was also the place where they could hear about possible jobs and especially printers had an easy time of getting work everywhere. Email from Morten Thing, Nov. 21, 2001; Lujo Brentano, *On the History and Development of Gilds and the Origin of Trade Unions* 89-90 (1870); *Ordbog over det danske Sprog* 6:912-13 (5th ed.; Copenhagen: Gyldendal, 1994 [1924]).

72 *Borås*: Sweden's eighth largest city with a population of 32,317 in 1925, it is 43 miles directly east of Gothenburg. Kungl. Statistisk Centralbyrån, *Årsbok för Sverige 1926*, tab. 10 at 8.

72 *"The Little Magician"*: A 48-page book with this title was published in Danish in Norway at the beginning of the century: *Den lille Tryllekunstner: en righoldig Samling af let udførlige, høist interessante og overraskende Tryllekunster til Underholdning i selskaber og gemytlige Kredse* (Kristiana [Oslo]: S. Kriedts Forlag, 1900).

77 *the Promenade des Anglais*: A wide road running the length of the Mediterranean sea-front in Nice and lined with turn-of-the-century grand hotels.

78 *Cagnes sur mer*: Located on the French Riviera between Antibes and Monte Carlo.

79 *Øresund*: The strait between the island of Zealand and Sweden connecting the Kattegat and the Baltic.

79 *Tårbæk*: A coastal town just north of Copenhagen with a well-known sailing harbor.

79 *Juan les Pins*: The town adjacent to Antibes on the Riviera.

79 *cacahuet*: The Spanish word for peanut; the French word is cacahouette or cacahuète.

80 *St. Tropez*: It lies further west along the Riviera.

80 *Toulon*: A larger coastal city near Marseille.

80 *bouillabaisse*: A specialty of Provence, where Marseille is located.

80 *La Corniche*: "The coastal road" winds along the Mediterranean coast and all the fanciest villas are located in this district.

82 *Hobro*: A medium-sized town in northern Jutland at the inland end of Mariager Fjord.

83 *Roskilde*: A town about 20 miles west of Copenhagen noted for its cathedral, where the Danish kings and queens are buried.

84 *I was charged with vagrancy*: Presumably Klitgaard was charged under The Vagrancy Act, 1824, which in the 1920s empowered a justice of the peace to commit every person convicted of "wandering abroad, or placing himself or herself in any public place, street, highway, court, or passage, to beg or gather alms . . . to the house of correction, there to be kept to hard labour for any time not exceeding one calendar month." The Vagrancy Act, 1924, 5 Geo. 4, ch. 83, § 3, in *The Complete Statutes of England: "Halsbury's Statutes of England"* 12: 913, 914 (London: Butterworth, 1930).

84 *Pourquoi non*: *Why Not.*

85 *outskirts of towns*: In the course of their migrations around the country, vagabonds stopped off in small towns and suburbs, gathering at cafes and in public squares.

86 *"Inky pinky parlez vous"*: A World War I British soldiers' song.

86 *toilet bowl . . . shouting*: The inmates forced the water down through the bowl siphon and onto the other side of the toilet trap; because the toilets in the cells were connected by means of this pipe, which led to the sewer, when the bowls were empty, they acted as a kind of megaphone. So-called toilet telephones are a worldwide phenomenon in prisons. At San Quentin state prison in California in the 1970s they worked this way: "The musings were broken by a rhythmic thumping through the concrete ceiling. He was wanted on the 'telephone.' He signaled back by standing on the toilet and pounding with the heel of his hand. Quickly he folded both blankets into squares, put them over the mouth of the seatless toilet, sat down and began jumping—forcing the water out. He scooped the last of it into the sink and kneeled at the toilet, his face in the bowl. 'Hallo!' he yelled. 'Who's on the phone?'" Edward Bunker, *Animal Factory* 148 (New York: Viking, 1977).

87 *hauled*: The ship had been hauled to the middle of the artificial basin by means of a rope or warp attached to a fixed object.

87 *Malmö*: Sweden's third largest city with a population of 116,348 in 1925, it is located on the coast directly across the Sound from Copenhagen. Kungl. Statistisk Centralbyrån, *Årsbok för Sverige 1926*, tab. 10 at 8.

87 *Norrköping*: Sweden's fourth largest city with a population of 60,132 in 1925, it is located about 100 miles southwest of Stockholm. Kungl. Statistisk Centralbyrån, *Årsbok för Sverige 1926*, tab. 10 at 8.

87 *Nykøping*: A smaller town (population 12,181 in 1925) located between Norrköping and Stockholm. Kungl. Statistisk Centralbyrån, *Årsbok för Sverige 1926*, tab. 10 at 8.

88 *the alcohol monopoly company*: The *spritbolag* was a system that became generalized in Sweden as a result of a statute enacted in 1917 that went into effect on January 1, 1919. Förordning angående försäljning av rusdrucker, in *Svensk Författningssamling*, 1917, No. 340, at 803-25. Under it, the sale to individuals of drinks with an alcohol content greater than 3.6 percent was limited exclusively to the "system company" (*systembolag*), which the State controlled and which paid almost all its profits to the State. Everyone who wished to buy alcohol for home consumption was registered and received a pass-book or ration book (*motbok*); the total amount of distilled spirits (defined as containing 22 percent alcohol) that they were permitted to buy each month was four liters. "The amount of alcohol which may be sold to a customer in a restaurant is also strictly limited and confined to mealtimes." *The Encyclopædia Britannica: The New Volumes* 32:630. After Sweden narrowly voted against prohibition in a referendum in 1922 (49.3% voting for prohibition and 50.7% voting against), a rationing system (called the Bratt System after Dr. Ivar Bratt) introduced in Stockholm on Feb. 26, 1914 and in force in all of the country since 1919, remained in effect: "The Bratt System was based on a strict licensing procedure for restaurants with extensive veto rights for local authorities, and individual rations for adult citizens to secure that each individual wasn't allowed to buy more than one could consume without harm for oneself or one's family. In practice this meant that the wealthy were allowed to buy more than the poor, and men allowed to buy more than women. Except for at restaurants, the purchases were noted in individual passbooks (*motbok*) which like bank-books were to be presented at the liquor store. Wine, beer and distilled liquors were sold by the glass only in connection with meals and only at licensed restaurants and cafés—and sold in bottles only by the Systembolaget's monopoly liquor stores. The Bratt rationing system was abolished in 1955, but the monopoly for sale of liquors, wine and beers (with more than 2.8% alcohol) still remains." "Swedish History: 1914-45," on http://www.

lysator.org/nordic/scn/faq736.html.

88 *on the tramp*: Travelling journeymen wandered from place to place (*på luffen*), especially abroad, to work for shorter or longer periods of time. *Ordbog over det danske Sprog* 13:2 (5th ed.; Copenhagen: Gyldendal, 1995 [1932]).

89 *Valdemarsvik*: A town located about 30 miles southeast of Norrköping at the inland end of a bay.

89 *chair sled*: The *sparkstøtting* (kick sled or chair toboggan), which dates back to the nineteenth century, remains a popular mode of transportation and recreation in Norway and Sweden. It is even used on icy city sidewalks by elderly people as a kind of walker in which to cart their groceries about.

92 *Gävle, Sundsvall, Umeå, Skellefteå, and Haparanda*: Swedish coastal towns stretching in order along the Gulf of Bothnia all the way to the Finnish border. It is almost 700 miles from Stockholm to Haparanda.

92 *Härnösand and Örnsköldsvik*: Two coastal towns located between Sundsvall and Umeå.

93 *Norrskensflamman: The Flame of the Northern Lights* was founded in 1906 and evolved from being a social-democratic into a left-wing socialist and, from 1922 on, a communist newspaper published six days a week in the far northern town of Luleå; in the early 1920s this four to eight page newspaper had a circulation of 11,000. http://www.kb.se/nl/titlar/128.htm.

93 *banking*: Raising the outer edge of a bend in the track counteracts the centrifugal force.

94 *people have put their index finger on their temple and buzzed like a bee*: The European equivalent of circling the temple with the index finger to indicate that someone is crazy.

94 *Østre Park*: Eastern Park (*Anlæg*) in Copenhagen, which was built in the 1870s on the military ramparts that had recently been removed, is located adjacent to the Botanic Garden; it is dotted with lakes and home to two art museums.

97 *Luleå*: Northern Sweden's principal town, it is the eastern terminus of the iron ore railroad and export port on the Gulf of Bothnia for Swedish iron ore. Its population in 1925 was 10,971. Kungl. Statistisk Centralbyrån, *Årsbok för Sverige 1926*, tab. 10 at 8.

98 *Laholm*: Located on Sweden's west coast, about one-third of the way between Malmö and Gothenburg.

101 *a Swedish mile*: 10 kilometers or about 6.2 miles.

103 *Kiruna*: Located in the far north (Lapland), about 100 miles south of Sweden's northernmost point, it is the northernmost municipality. Not founded until 1899, when it was connected to the railway carrying iron ore to Narvik (Norway) and Luleå, its population grew like that of a Klondike gold-rush town during its first two decades, reaching 7,500 by 1910. According to Klitgaard's diary entries from 1926, he arrived in Kiruna in the summer of 1924. Leon Jaurnow, *Den lyse vagabond: Mogens Klitgaards liv og forfatterskab* 28 (Copenhagen: Reitzel, 2002 [forthcoming]).

103 *mountains*: The general Danish word for "mountain" is *bjerg*; the word used here, *fjeld*, denotes tall mountains consisting of rock masses, especially those whose tops are above the tree line, and applies only to formations outside of Denmark.

103 *Kirunavaara*: Located within the city limits, it is the world's largest iron ore mine.

103 *billiard pins*: The game here is a unique Danish specialty, developed about a century ago, called pin-billiards (*keglebillard*), which involves 5 pins placed in a diamond shape at the center of the table. The point is to hit the red ball against the white ball, which in turn must knock over the pins in the middle. If the red ball knocks over a pin, the player gets minus points. A player keeps playing as long as he keeps knocking over pins or hitting both white balls with the red ball.

104 *Narvik*: An ice-free port in northern Norway to which iron ore from Kiruna began to be transported by rail in the late nineteenth century. The towns are about 85 miles apart. Founded in 1883 as Victoriahavn, it became a town in 1902. At the census of 1920 its population was only 6,499. Statistiske Centralbyrå, *Statistisk Årbok for Kongeriket Norge 1921*, tab. 3 at 10 (Kristiana: Aschehoug, 1922).

104 *Teddy*: "There was a tobacco war going on nearly 100 years ago . . . and it arrived [in] Norway soon after the British-American Tobacco Co. (Norway) Ltd. was established in Oslo 1905. It rapidly became a cruel war between the American tobacco trust (led by American Tobacco Company's James 'Buck' Duke) and the Norwegian manufacturers. In U.S.A. president Theodore 'Teddy' Roosevelt was fighting the American trust/enterprise, and he soon became a kind of hero for the Norwegian manufacturers. In 1914 J. L. Tiedemann's Tobaksfabrik honored Roosevelt by launching a cigarette brand named TEDDY. The trust war in Norway ended in November/December 1930 when BAT (Norway) was split between BATCO (45%), Tiedemann (45%), DnC (5%) - a bank, Andresens Bank (5%) - a bank owned by the Andresen family, the real owners of J. L. Tiedemanns Tobaksfabrik, when A/S Norsk-Engelsk Tobakkfabrikk (NETO) was established. In November 1933 NETO was completely in the hands of J. L. Tiedemanns . . . ." Roosevelt's image also appeared on the package. "A Brief History of Teddy," on http://home.online.no/~smpeders/ind-ted. htm.

104 *tobacco monopoly*: In 1914 the Swedish parliament introduced a state monopoly, AB Svenska Tobaksmonopolet, which went into effect in 1915. Förordning angående statsmonopol å tobakstillverkningen i riket, in *Svensk Författningssamling* No. 436, at 1355 (1914).

104 *Gällivare*: A town 50 miles south of Kiruna.

105 *rømmekolle*: A Norwegian dish made of curdled whole milk strewn with sugar and crumbs; it is a dessert, but it is unlikely that people in Narvik were eating it while walking around. Neither the word nor the dish is widely known in Denmark.

107 *the sea*: Narvik is situated on a fjord, which is connected to the Norwegian Sea, which in turn connects the Atlantic Ocean and the Barents Sea.

108 *The engineer told tall tales about back when he'd built a railroad in Persia*: Construction of the Trans-Iranian Railway began in the 1927; after delays with British and U.S. contractors, a Swedish-Danish syndicate took over construction. Julian Bharier, *Economic Development in Iran 1900-1970*, at 202-206 (London: Oxford University Press, 1971).

108 *Spitsbergen*: An island (and also a group of islands) in the Arctic Ocean north of the Norwegian mainland; in 1920 the dispute between the Soviet Union and Norway over the islands was resolved in favor of Norway, which incorporated them in 1925.

111 *a big power station*: This hydroelectric plant, which was one of the first built by the Swedish state in 1915, was designed to provide power to the iron ore industry.

112 *I became a wholesale smuggler*: Klitgaard wrote a story about this episode in his life: Mogens Klitgaard, "Teddy-smugleren," in *Social-Demokraten: Hjemmets Søndag*, Mar. 20, 1938, republished in Mogens Klitgaard: *Hverdagens musik; Udvalgte noveller og skitser* 27-

34 (Sven Møller Kristensen ed.; Copenhagen: Fremad, 1989).

113 *Malmberget*: The Ore Mountain, it is located about a mile outside Gällivare.

113 *Piteå*: Also located on the Gulf of Bothnia a little south of Luleå.

114 *Umeå*: A town on the Gulf of Bothnia south of Piteå, its population was 7,002 in 1920. Statistisk Centralbyrån, *Årsbok för Sverige 1939*, tab. 10 at 8 (Stockholm: Norstedt, 1939).

116 *Östersund*: A town located in the center of central Sweden with a population in 1925 of 14,552. Kungl. Statistisk Centralbyrån, *Årsbok för Sverige 1926*, tab. 10 at 8.

118 *Vesterbro Street*: Vesterbrogade is a main artery running from Frederiksberg Gardens into the center of Copenhagen near City Hall. In 1935 (and from the beginning of the twentieth century) it was the third most populous street in Copenhagen; Klitgaard lived in a garret on Vesterbrogade in 1936 while writing *There's a Man Sitting on a Trolley.* Københavns statistiske Kontor, *Statistisk Aarbog for København, Frederiksberg og Gjentofte Kommune 1936-1937*, tab. 11 at 11 (Copenhagen: Bianco Luno, 1937); Mow., "Min Bog var for mig Knald eller Fald—siger Mogens Klitgaard," *Berlingske Aftenavis*, June 9, 1937.

118 *Deer Park*: Jægersborg Dyrehave in Klampenborg 6 miles north of Copenhagen is an enclosed forest, which dates back to 1669 when King Frederik III had a smaller deer park created on that site. It is a very popular recreational site.

118 *Studenterkilden*: An old restaurant on the southern border of Deer Park. Earlier it had been known for catering to students.

118 *Lake Bagsværd*: Located northwest of Copenhagen.

119 *Abisko*: Abisko National Park, which was established in 1909, is located northwest of Kiruna, near the Norwegian border and Narvik.

121 *Wedding*: A working-class neighborhood in Berlin, often known as Roter (Red) Wedding.

122 *Gare du Nord*: A railway station in Paris, at which, as the name implies, trains arrive from northern Germany and Scandinavia.

122 *it occurred to me that in a few days I'd be thirty years old. And that was the ridiculous thought that . . . wouldn't leave me alone*: Klitgaard himself experienced such an epiphany on his thirtieth birthday, prompting him to write *There's a Man Sitting on a Trolley*. See above "Introduction" at pp. xvii-xviii.

123 *Magasin du Nord*: A large Danish department store.

125 *rue Servandoni*: William Faulkner lived on this street in 1925. http://www.uhb.fr/faulkner/WF/centenial/four. htm.

126 *Bois de Boulogne*: The transformation of a state forest into the first large municipal park in Paris in the 1850s was projected and managed by Napoléon III and Baron Haussman; the 865-hectare Bois de Boulogne lies on the western edge of Paris. David Pinkney, *Napoleon III and the Rebuilding of Paris* 94-99 (Princeton: Princeton University Press, 1972).

126 *La vie parisienne*: A well-known weekly magazine, published from 1863 until 1949, "it won a firm foothold by being very well informed on women's fashions and on Paris gossip . . . , but it attracted male readers by dealing with these subjects in a titillating way. Its most successful issues were reprinted as mild pornography, but just mild enough to escape prosecution." Theodore Zeldin, *France, 1848-1945*, vol. 2: *Intellect, Taste and Anxiety* 717 (Oxford: Clarendon, 1977). For hundreds of examples of pictures of women in the magazine in the 1920s, see *The Girls from La Vie Parisienne* (N.p. [New York?]: Citadel, 1961); *French Fashion Illustrations of the Twenties: 634 Cuts from La Vie Parisienne* (Carol Grafton ed.; New York: Dover, 1987).

127 *Flag*: A very popular cigarette in the 1920s. Jørgen Sømod, "Sønderjylland umiddelbart efter 1920," on http://www.gladsaxegym nasium.dk/2/soemod/fpenge.htm.

127 *I . . . was deported from the Kingdom of Sweden for all time*: Klitgaard in fact was in Umeå looking for new sales territories for his smuggling operation when he was deported (but probably not permanently) from Sweden on November 9, 1924, for lacking the prescribed passport and the ability to support himself. Leon Jaurnow, *Den lyse vagabond* at 30. When Klitgaard fled to Sweden from Denmark and the Gestapo in August 1943, a friend mentioned to a newspaper that Klitgaard in his younger days had been a smuggler in northern Sweden; he was then briefly imprisoned and released. Sven Møller Kristensen, "Indledning," in Mogens Klitgaard, *Hverdagens musik: Udvalgte noveller og skitser* 7-11 at 7-8 (Sven Møller Kristensen ed.; Copenhagen: Fremad, 1989).

127 *salt and bread make your cheeks red*: *Salt og brød gør kinden rød* is a an old Danish saying that Klitgaard uses ironically to mean that poor people are supposed to be consoled by the thought that they can live healthily on salt and bread alone. A history of working-class life in Denmark's second largest city, which bears the saying as its title, quotes the written recollections of a machinist who had been an errand boy for a baker in Århus in the 1890s from whom he once in a while received "old bread, which, no matter how old it was, was always welcome. Undernourished as we were, we were always hungry. Many times our evening meal was dry rye bread with salt and tea to go with it. My mother had a slogan, which went: Salt and bread make your cheeks red. It was always at the end of the week that we heard it, when the lard had run out—we didn't know about butter." Svend Aage Andersen, *Salt og brød gør kinden rød: Arbejderliv i Århus 1870-1940*, at 91 (Århus: Universitetsforlaget, 1985).